LEAD IN THE V

An Account of the History and Deve.
Lead Mining in the Parishes
Great Hucklow, Little Hucklow and Grindlow,
and how it shaped the landscape and the lives of the people.

Compiled, written and designed by Parishioners of
Great Hucklow
2009

This Book is part of a larger project to record the lead mining heritage of the modern combined parish of Great Hucklow, in the Hundred of the High Peak, Derbyshire.

Other elements of the project will include a Lead Trail leaflet for visitors to follow, interpretation boards placed at significant sites, and a website outlining the lead mining features of the parish.

There will be an ongoing compilation of archive material which will be held and made available for future public access.

The project is also running in parallel with the Silence Heritage Site – an area of wildlife and lead mining archaeological interest held in trust and administered by the Parishes of Great Hucklow and Foolow.

'Lead In The Veins'

Published by

Hucklow Publishing

for and on behalf of

© **Great Hucklow & District Community Spirit Committee**

September 2009

ISBN 978-0-9563473-0-5

Hucklow Publishing
Ash House
Great Hucklow
Derbyshire
SK17 8RF

Printed in Great Britain by
Hammer Design
Hathersage Business Park
Hathersage
Derbyshire
S32 1DP

This Project has been made possible by the generous financial help provided in the form of a grant from

Contents

The Great Hucklow Lead Mining Liberties

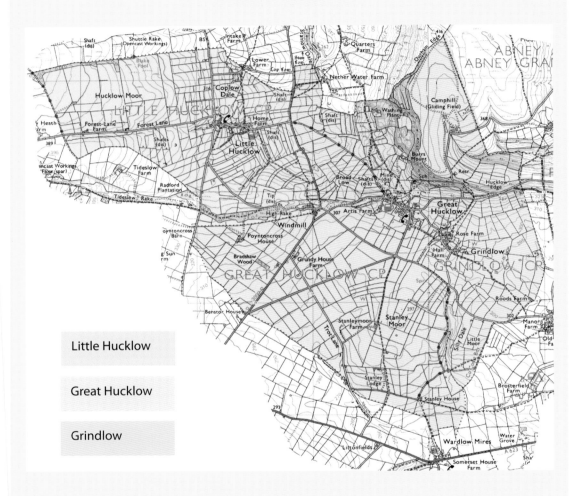

Little Hucklow

Great Hucklow

Grindlow

Modern map showing the Civil Parishes of Little Hucklow, Great Hucklow and Grindlow.

The boundaries of these parishes follow those of the old Lordships which had Manorial Rights held in possession by a Lord of the Manor.

These boundaries were also those of the lead mining Liberties, each Liberty having jurisdiction over the rights and privileges of miners operating in that defined area.

This book is dedicated to the memory of the Free Miners of the High Peak
'A rude and boorish kind of people' (Daniel Defoe)

The 17th and 18th Centuries gentry who visited The Peak perceived it as a wild and desolate place inhabited by rude, boorish people resembling troglodytes. But it was this land which produced the finest lead ore in Britain to make their pewter vessels, embellish their houses and manufacture lead shot for their armies – ore mined and worked by those same 'rude and boorish' people. Although the great landowners such as the Cavendishes (Dukes of Devonshire) and the Manners (Dukes of Rutland) benefitted hugely from the exploitation of the mineral veins on their land, their class showed little regard for the miners who actually won the ore from the ground.

William Hooson, a miner from Youlgreave, produced '*The Miner's Dictionary'* in 1747 to counter the opinions of those *'who reap great benefit from their* (the miner's) *Endeavours to be a set of disposable Men of no good Characters, but Tools to be employed on Occasions in the Mines and a great deal more to brand them with.'*

He concludes his book:

'Whether there be any Practical Miners that have written anything of mining, is more than I yet know, but several Gentlemen have furnished us with bits and scrips taken on Information mixt and wrought up with (perhaps) some guesswork of their own: but I do not see that a Man is either the wiser or better for them, for what I have delivered is the very Practice as the Experienced Miner well know . . . If any shall object against my Rough, yet Plain way of Writing &c., he may easily excuse me, when I tell him, I always was, am and hope by God's help so to continue the remainder of my days a MINER.'

By dint of effort, skill, intelligence and determination the miners set up their own progressive and enlightened religious movements, self-help ways to education, and a modicum of social welfare. The freedom to prospect for, find, work and develop a lucrative lead mine was one way out of the grinding poverty of the time, and the freedom to do it against the unsympathetic vested interests of the established landlords was a powerful driving force for this 'rude and boorish' people.

It was these same free miners of The Peak who by dint of resilience and determination attempted to defended their ancient customs by codifying the laws of the Barmote Courts against the interests of the wealthier classes. In the end, the vested interests of ownership combined with financial power, the development of new technology and efficient exploitation of mineral ore elsewhere saw the eventual and rapid demise of the Free Miners of the High Peak. To them we dedicate this book.

18th Century miners at work drilling a shot hole by candle-light

(Science Museum/Science and Society Library)

Lead in the Veins

From at least the time of the Roman occupation the winning of lead ore from the earth has been an important activity of the Hucklow area, and it is only during the last 120 years that lead mining and its related activities have not been the principal way of life for most of its inhabitants.

As the years go by there are fewer signs that such a major activity ever existed; mine buildings have been dismantled and the materials reclaimed, spoil heaps removed and reprocessed, and the natural environment has done its best to obliterate what remains above ground with trees, shrubs, bramble and bracken. Only the discerning eye will recognise in fields of pasture, the tell-tale humps and hillocks of ancient mining activity, the occasional capped mine shaft, and tracks and trails apparently leading nowhere and for no purpose, which were once the essential miners' paths and lead roads. These are now the only tangible signs that here was once a centuries-old industry that modified the landscape and developed a way of life, language and livelihood for generations bounded by the dictates of the mine and mining law.

There may be little to see on the surface, but beneath our wonderful patchwork of stone-walled fields, woods and coppices, the streams, roads and farmsteads, an 'other' world of the old lead miner is locked in perpetual darkness, a veritable maze of levels, soughs, shafts and turns – hundreds of miles of tunnels hacked and chiselled through the living rock to win the precious payload of metal-bearing ore from its veins, pipes and ribs. Below our feet only the ghost of "T'owd Mon" lingers in his grave-dark soughs, stopes and levels, perhaps accompanied by the 'knockers', the very spirits of the veins which he mined.

It is from the beginning of the medieval period that lead mining began to develop here as a significant industry; such a long period of sustained and specialised activity cannot help but leave its mark, not only on the environment but on the community. Tradition, law and custom produced a vocabulary peculiar to lead miners' way of life. Many of the words and expressions of this language are still in use, but most, like the above-ground remnants of our mining past, have withered into the obscurity of our collective history, although they are still redolent with the echoes of that time when there was 'lead in the veins'.

As well as such lead mining terms as levels and soughs, miners spoke of bucking irons, bootits and bowse, of cadge, caulk, cope and cranch, of doorsteads and dot holes, of edgeboards and eyes, of fothers and founder shafts, of garlands and green linnets, of hard beds and hoppets, of idlepegs and inning, of lidstones and mandrells, of nittings and nogers, of pees and pump trees, of rowling water, screwstones, Tollman's Dots, underbeats, whimseys and yoakings.

We have included a short Glossary which gives a brief explanation for those mining words and

Hucklow Edge from Litton

expressions used in the text; a more detailed listing of lead mining terms can be found in 'A Glossary of Derbyshire Lead Mining Terms' by Dr JH Rieuwerts, and published by the Peak District Mines Historical Society Ltd, to which we are indebted for our information.

The intention of this book is to provide an overview of the lead mining heritage of this small Peakland Parish, to identify and record the remnants of that heritage at the beginning of this third Millennium before they disappear entirely from local memory.

Of enormous help in writing the historical sections of the book is the vast amount of information on the lead mines of the Eyam area collected over many years by DA Nash and Dr JS Beck. This entire collection of some 3,000 documents has been made available to us as a permanent record and will be held as a part of a Parish archive along with the other material and evidence collected by the compilers of the various sections of the book.

We are also greatly indebted to Dr John Barnatt, Senior Survey Archeologist for the Peak District National Park Authority, and Dr JH Rieuwerts both of whom have given us so much help and encouragement in the initial stages of the project and have continued to assist us in bringing it all to fruition. Dr Rieuwerts' unbounded enthusiasm, his encyclopaedic knowledge of lead mining history, and his many publications on the subject have been of enormous use to us. We owe much

too to Nellie Kirkham whose paper on the Great Hucklow mines first inspired us to produce this book and who did such extensive field work in the 1950s-60s before much of what remained was lost through natural decay and regeneration.

Also of great help to us in understanding the social and political history of the area has been Andy Wood's book, 'The Politics of Social Conflict: The Peak District 1520-1770'.

Without the financial assistance given to us in the form of a grant from the Lottery Heritage Fund, to whom we are profoundly grateful, this book would never have seen the light of day, and we would like to pay tribute to their generosity and encouragement in what has been a fascinating journey for those involved.

We have been overwhelmed by the amount of information to be found in various libraries and elsewhere and regret that space and the time schedule has restricted our research. However, we hope that this book and the archive we are collecting will serve as a spur to future historians. We are indebted to many members of the parish of Great Hucklow and District who have given of their time and expertise to make this project possible.

Our book is not intended to be an academic treatise of our lead mining heritage, but rather an accessible and general companion of information for those interested in the topography of the locality and its industrial, social and natural histories. And we hope you enjoy it as such.

1. Muscle, Grit and Candlelight
– a brief history of Derbyshire Lead Mining

As lead mining in Great Hucklow was part of an important industry which once ranged over the whole Derbyshire orefield it would be useful to look briefly at some aspects of its history.

There is some evidence that lead ore (galena) was smelted in Derbyshire some 3500 years ago. The Romans in the first century AD established the beginnings of lead mining as an important industry in the area. Demand for lead grew apace during the Mediaeval period and for the 200 years up to 1780 the Peak District of Derbyshire was probably one of the most important lead mining areas in the world. By the 1600s the lead industry had become second only to the wool trade in its importance to the national economy.

'Opencast' mining in Europe depicted by Agricola in his 'De Re Metallica' (1556). Note the diviner with hazel stick.

In those days lead was an essential commodity not only for covering the roofs of ancient churches and cathedrals but also for the new grand houses of the nobility and gentry. Even the humbler farms and cottages were making increasing use of lead glazing bars in their windows, and it was the only relatively inexpensive material available for lining water storage tanks and piping. As well as this home market there was also a thriving export trade and Derbyshire lead was exported mainly from Hull via the docks at Bawtry, and later by canal from Chesterfield to the River Trent.

The many uses of lead at that time would be similar to the ways we use plastics nowadays. There were the obvious functions such as roofs, gutters and down pipes, water cisterns, supply pipes, sinks and drains, but also it was much used in making weights for scales, milk pans, pewter ware, lining for storage containers, paint and pottery glazes, medicine and musket balls. Its general use as an active ingredient for medicines might seem strange to us today, but even more alarming is that compounds of lead were used in vast quantities to whiten bread and to make wine appear sweeter. It is little wonder then that lead mining was a boom industry.

From the most ancient of times lead ore was in general regarded as Crown property (as was any mineral commodity won by any means from beneath the ground) and the Crown controlled all areas of Derbyshire bearing lead ore. These were known as the Kings/Queensfield and had two separately administered divisions, the High and Low Peaks. Each of these was further divided into smaller Liberties based on the ancient boundaries of manors or lordships, although a few of these were independent of the laws governing the Kings/Queesfield.

Every aspect of the lead mining industry – the activities of miners themselves, the sale and smelting of the ore and the legal mechanisms for establishing title and ownership – all stemmed from this ancient claim by the monarch to all mineral rights. Over the centuries the whole structure was developed into a means by which the Duchy of Lancaster, a Royal possession, could extract as much revenue (then called the King's royalties) as possible from the industry. This it did by means of 'farming out' title and permission to mine for minerals, and the miners paid their duty to the 'King's farmer'. The Barmaster was the executive officer of the Barmote Court, assisted by deputies responsible for the Liberties and by a jury of local miners (the Body of the Mine); he oversaw the day to day running of the industry and was responsible for summoning the Court.

It was also in the interest of the Crown to encourage miners to explore for more deposits of ore and expand their activities, and this resulted in two enduring characteristic features of the industry:

1. The Barmaster would allow any person to open a mine and retain title to it as long as they could show that they had discovered a significant amount of lead ore and would continue to work the mine and produce lead

2. No landowner, tenant or user of the surface of the land could interfere with or attempt to prevent lead mining activities in the Dutchy land

These two rules alone were no doubt chiefly responsible for the incredibly complicated and convoluted laws governing lead mining which developed over the centuries, and which in a way became part of the reason for its ultimate demise. Tradition and time-honoured self-interested restrictive practices became hallmarks of the industry, but the 'laws' also became more and more difficult to apply in the 19th Century as modern mechanised mining techniques took over from the ancient ways of pick and shovel, muscle, grit and candle-light.

By the 1890s lead mining as an industry was all but finished in most of the Derbyshire ore field, although a few mines did struggle on into the 20th Century. The last large lead mine was Millclose Mine near Matlock which closed in 1940.

Today some of those mines are still active, such as Mill Dam Mine in Great Hucklow, but the prize here is not principally lead ore but fluorspar and calcite – minerals used in a wide variety of modern products from toothpaste to plastics, paint, ceramics, North Sea drilling and in steel and aluminium refining

Although the lead mining industry is long gone, evidence for its past is all around us. The families who derived fortunes from lead duties built the great country houses of the nobility such as Chatsworth, Haddon, Hardwick. The gentry's residences, such as Eyam Hall and Hucklow Hall, were financed from profits gained as partners in mining ventures, as shareholders or even lead merchants and mine agents. Whole villages grew up where the miners lived, such as Bradwell and Eyam, as well as smaller ones such as Peak Forest and our own villages of the Hucklows and Grindlow, where there is still evidence of the lead miners' tiny cottages separated by winding footpaths and genels (a passage between houses).

At a lowlier level, although less obvious, are the remains of old workings scattered over pasture and woodland, of old barns or 'coes' erected by miners in fields adjacent to their workings, of the 'bole hills' in the area used for early smelting activities, and the later remains of smelting mills and cupolas. In places such as Tideslow Rake it is possible to see the old 'opencast' workings and more recently produced hillocks of spoil, and from June to August discover a small bushy plant with star-like flowers, the metalophytic leadwort which will grow where other plants cannot survive because of the presence of lead in the soil.

In areas such as Hucklow Edge there remain signs of where the mine shafts existed and still possible to tread the miners' ways and footpaths which thread their way between them.

The landscape, topography and social history of this part of Derbyshire are synonymous with the history and development of the lead mining industry, and the following sections attempt to trace it in brief outline.

Early History

*(Most of the material for the following sections is adapted from Dr JH Rieuwerts' introduction to **'Lead Mining in the Peak District'** published by Peak District Mines Historical Society Ltd.)*

Evidence found in Early Bronze Age barrows in Derbyshire shows that these early inhabitants used lead at least in the form of beads well before the arrival of the Romans.

The Romans definitely worked the ore field and

much evidence is in existence in the form of lead 'pigs' or ingots which have been unearthed and bear the original Roman markings which designate them as coming from the Derbyshire area.

Extraction of lead ore by the Romans would probably be confined to open workings along the outcrops of the major veins. These veins would have been up to 40 yards wide at the surface and although not exclusively filled with lead ore the workings could be taken to a fair depth by open-cast methods. No doubt the Romans possessed the knowledge and technical skill required to undertake deep mining, but open-cast working would have been a far more economical proposition, particularly as they would probably be dependant on local unskilled labour for the actual work.

The local Roman military presence was at Anavio, a fortification at the river crossing at Brough, built in 78-79AD and garrisoned by the First Cohort of Aquitanians. The Romans eventually developed Anavio into a more substantial fort possibly to protect Roman lead mining interests as well as to secure the trading routes and military roads which criss-crossed the area. The fort was abandoned in the fourth century but traces of the headquarters building can still be seen; there is evidence of a substantial 'vicus', a civilian settlement outside a fort, now for the most part covered by the large range of buildings on the opposite side of the road from Brough Mill.

Lead mining declined after the Romans left Britain when demand for lead dropped and although there is not much archaeological evidence for mining in Anglo-Saxon times, yet many of the terms which remained in use over the centuries had their origins in pre-Norman Anglo-Saxon period. For example, the available lead ore

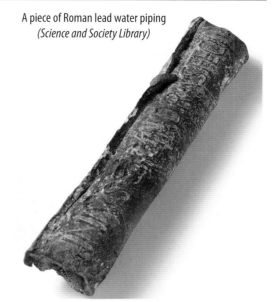

A piece of Roman lead water piping
(Science and Society Library)

at that time would have occurred much nearer the surface and was worked downwards in a groove or 'grove', an early English word which also came to mean the site of a mine – and a word which still persists in many of the lead mine names, and has the same derivation as the word 'grave'; the same word is also related to our local word 'grough', a steep sided channel cut through the peat of the moorlands.

After the withdrawal of the Romans from Britain there is little evidence of mining activities for some 600 years. From the Norman Conquest there begins to be far more documentary evidence of lead mining in Derbyshire. During the intervening period both the Saxons and the Danes filtered into the Peakland hills, and although mining continued it was on a smaller scale than previously. It was, however, during this time that mining law began to be formalised and the product of the mines within the Kings/Queensfield became the lawful property of the Crown to whom the miners paid mineral duties. . This has continued to be the case even to the present day, although the Duchy of Lancaster has collected the duties since late Mediaeval times.

The village of Great Hucklow is an ancient High Peak settlement which the Norman scribes felt was worth a mention in the Doomsday Book, but was

Roman pig of lead found near the fort at Brough

no doubt in existence long before the Normans took an interest.

From 1100 onwards lead became in far greater demand as the great castles, churches and religious houses needed vast quantities of lead for their roofs, not only in this country but in France as well – about 100 tons of British lead was sent to Clairvaux Abbey in the late 12th Century.

Accounts indicate that the mining was widespread and well established throughout the orefield during this period. Tideslow mines on Tideswell Moor (at the western end of the Hucklow Edge Rake) were worked in 1195 and between 1216 and 1249, producing some 13000 loads in the period, or about 400 loads per annum (4 loads = 1 ton). Remaining mines in the High Peak (which includes Hucklow) yielded almost 1000 loads each year between 1236 and 1249.

In 1288 in Ashbourne an Inquisition or 'Quo Warranto' was held whose purpose was to set down in writing some, though not all, of the contemporary customs of the Derbyshire leadminers. It was stated that some of the customs 'hath been used time out of memory of man' indicating that these laws and customs already had an ancient lineage. There is considerable weight of opinion among mining historians that these laws originated in the folkmeets or gemotes of Anglo-Saxon England over a thousand years ago.

The document itself, sometimes known as 'The Miner's Bible', became the basis for the governing of all lead mining activities in the following centuries. Although lead mining died out as a significant activity in the late 19th Century, those laws and customs still exist as enacted by statute in the 1851 Mineral Laws and are embodied in the proceedings of the Barmote Courts. These courts continue to have some jurisdiction in the Derbyshire lead mining Liberties.

Mediaeval Period

Mining continued to flourish and grow through the Mediaeval period, carried on for the most part by individuals or small groups of miners digging where they could and for what was easiest to win. The methods and technology of ore extraction progressed slowly over the next three hundred years, underground exploitation being developed by a variety of methods in localised areas of the

Derbyshire ore field and tools modified to suit the task. Those most often used were the poll-pick or stone pick, having one end pointed and the other squared – the square end was struck with a heavy hammer, the pointed end being used in the fashion of a drill bit. A variety of picks, chisels, mauls (heavy hammer), gadds (large wedges) and other tools were developed for specialist use in ore extraction and these gradually came into more general use.

Fire-setting' was often used to crack the rock of a working face to make it easier to break up with the wedges. For this a fire was built against the rock face which was fractured and sometimes shattered from the heat generated by the fire over several hours. The fumes and smoke often affected adjacent workings as through the course of time they often became linked by obsolete tunnels, or by natural cracks and cave fissures. The increased use of fire-setting meant that new laws had to be introduced by the Barmote Courts to prevent the danger of suffocation in neighbouring mines. It was ruled that fire-setting should take place only after 4pm, which was the official end of the mining day.

The ore gained from the mine was conveyed to the shaft or mine entrance either in baskets, called wiskets, or dragged over the uneven floor or 'sole' of the mine by means of a wooden sledge, known as a 'corve'. At the shaft the material was wound to the surface by a small windlass, or stowes, operated by one or two men.

Once the ore was on the surface then it had to be 'dressed' before it could be sold on for smelting. Much of the pure 'bing ore' obtained from the rich ribs and veins required little attention save for breaking it into manageable pieces which was done with a special hammer known as a 'bucking iron'. Poorer quality ore, called 'bouse', was taken for cleaning in water along the courses of many streams or rivers to produce what was known as 'wash ore'.

At this time the dressed ore was smelted in bole furnaces, usually sited on the tops of westward facing hills or scarp edges, so taking advantage of the prevailing winds to ventilate the fires. The furnace was a three-sided stone structure into which were placed alternate layers of wood and lead ore. Mediaeval boles were small, about three feet in diameter. Post Mediaeval boles were much larger, some up to twenty feet, but usually at each site there were only two or three hearths. Many of the local hills on which these furnaces were sited are still called 'Bole Hill'.

This type of smelting was not very efficient and even by the time of its demise in the early 17th Century efficiency had increased to not much more than 50%. The method was also very hungry for wood, which resulted in most of the ancient woodlands around the Hope Valley area being destroyed to satisfy the demand for fuel. A few patches of ancient scrub oak did survive, such as the area around Padley Gorge above Grindleford.

Ore dressing and washing methods also became more efficient by the end of the 16th Century; as demand for lead grew, washing was increasingly done on or close to the mine site and water was channelled by 'launders' into special washing troughs called 'buddles' and the whole process was known as 'buddling'. Ore was also dressed more efficiently by the use of large iron-clad stone wheels driven by horse power on a circular crushing floor.

An engraving from Agricola depicting the use of launders.

17th Century onwards

Matters became more serious and organised throughout the 17th and 18th Centuries as the demand for lead grew. Improved techniques of tunnelling, draining, of lifting the ore, early pumping and ventilation equipment all helped the miners to dig deeper and further and become more efficient. On the surface the processing of the ore became more refined, and the organisation of an improved financial investment system also helped in these developments.

Great Hucklow came to be an area of concentrated mining activity, sitting as it did on what was regarded as one of the richest veins of lead ore in the High Peak – one long 'rake' which stretched from beyond Tideslow Moor in the west to Eyam in the east.

A 'rake' is the name given to one of the principal forms of mineral deposit found in the Derbyshire orefields. Essentially it is a vertical fissure in rock strata formed as a fault structure during earth movements and subsequently filled with minerals bearing the lead ore (galena), amongst others. Most rakes consist of a series of parallel fractures occupying a zone which might be as much as fifty yards in width, and can be of considerable length, generally between two and five miles. No rake has ever been 'bottomed', but the payable mineralization is usually confined to the upper four to six hundred feet.

To give a measure of how rich the Hucklow Edge vein was, between the years 1697 and 1701 a total of 10,513 loads of lead ore was recovered from mines on Hucklow Edge, this by hand labour only. Within the Derbyshire orefield lead ore was measured in loads and dishes, a dish being 65lbs – nine dishes made a load, so that four loads were the equivalent of a ton of lead ore; therefore in those four years 2628 tons of lead ore were gained by miners working with hand tools and by the light of candles!

Around the middle of the 17th Century, Derbyshire miners adopted an excavation technique that was already well tried in the European Continental mines. The method sounds simple but in fact demanded great expertise for it to be effective in tunnelling through solid limestone, one of the hardest of natural rock

Modern reproduction of a horse gin winding drum
– Magpie Mine, Sheldon.

minerals. Although this method had been in use for many years to mine through zones of weakness or to extract ore, they now used it to construct long cross-cut levels in hard, relatively unjointed limestone by cutting a series of parallel grooves in the rock and then trimming the sides of the tunnel, or level, to make forward progress towards other veins of ore material. Progress was painfully slow, averaging about 1.5 inches (3.8cm) per shift in 1670, but attaining the break-neck speed of 3 inches per shift half a century later. It is no wonder that when gunpowder was introduced as a rock blasting technique it soon became very popular, and by the 1700s it was in use across most of the orefield. However, it did have its dangers, and as a pound of gunpowder based blasting powder cost the equivalent of a man's daily wage the older man-powered rock breaking techniques still continued alongside the new.

The 17th Century saw a great expansion and prosperity in the lead mining industry, which brought with it a much better organisation of mining methods and innovations of ore reclamation and smelting. It was also an important industry nationally. A petition handed in to Parliament in 1641-42 listed by name some 20,000 people who were miners, ore-dressers, carriers or others directly involved in the industry. 'Gentleman adventurers' became increasingly interested in investing in the industry and many partnerships were set up between them. Shares were taken in particular mining ventures, some of which meant the laying out of considerable sums of money before any return could be expected, although for the luckier ones these returns could be very handsome.

Some of the principal mines at work at this time were those on the Hucklow Edge Vein, pursuing the vein eastwards from Great Hucklow, ever deeper beneath the cap of shale. The Old Edge Grove and the New Edge Grove produced 8500 loads from 1683 until 1701, and the wealth of these two mines attracted lengthy lawsuits in the Barmote Court, but more particularly at the Duchy Court around 1695-1710.

The 17th, 18th and onwards into the 19th Centuries saw the greatest expansion of Derbyshire lead mining activities in terms of technological advance and ore production.

Wealthy merchants from all over the country as well the local lead merchants and smelters began to invest heavily in the gaining and production of lead. This injection of capital enabled mining in areas and to depths not previously possible by the small-scale part-time free miners with their limited manpower and technology.

Underground water had always been one of the limiting factors in mining to a depth and the effectiveness of man-powered 'rag and chain' pumps or raising barrels of water by means of a horse gin to keep abreast of the ingress of water was very limited. Water was pumped up to drainage tunnels or shale-gates by 1670, but the innovation of steam-driven pumps (about 1715) was a major development in mine drainage.

With the increasing knowledge and use of explosives it also became possible to drive long drainage soughs to 'unwater' mines that had too much water to be drained by pumping power. Before a sough was constructed the usual procedure was to make a legal agreement between the soughmaster and the proprietors of the mines that could be unwatered by tapping into the sough. Usually these mines were officially surveyed and the 'water marks' set at the lowest part of the mine free of water. The soughmasters received a certain proportion of the ore eventually gained from below these marks (usually between a quarter and a sixth).

As mines penetrated deeper into the earth it became necessary to improve ventilation, especially when mining under the shales where there was danger of methane gas. Many methods were devised in various parts of the ore field. The traditional method was to set a brazier of burning coals at the bottom of a shaft so that the rising column of warm air would draw fresh ventilation from other parts of the mine.

Investment encouraged the miners to extend several old and well tried veins such as the Hucklow Edge Vein. Previous to this time the vein had been worked mainly where the limestone was at the surface or had dipped just a little below the shale. This shale covering becomes progressively thicker as Hucklow Edge becomes Eyam Edge and in some parts a total thickness of 976 feet of shales and gritstone had to be sunk through before the underlying limestone was reached. Some of the main engine shafts of the mines on Eyam Edge were generally between 400 and 1000ft deep.

Between 1721 and 1739 over 19400 loads of ore were raised at Ladywash Mine giving the fortunate proprietors and their partners an overall profit of £8,500. Other mines along the extension of the Hucklow Vein on Eyam Edge were no less spectacular – Miners Engine (a little further to the west from Silence Mine) produced 10700 loads in the three years after 1733.

Ore dressing and smelting methods also improved. The major advance in the 18th Century was the introduction, about 1737, of the cupola furnace, or low arched reverberatory furnace. The innovation appears to have been made simultaneously but independently by the Bagshawe's and the London Lead Company.

The furnace was fired by coal, but the ore charge was separated from the fuel by a bridge inside the furnace, the flames being drawn into the ore compartment by draught provided by a combination of long flues and a high chimney. The principal cupola sites near to the Hucklow mines were the Lord's Mill Cupola at Middleton Dale, Birds Cupola on Bretton Edge, Middleton Dale Upper Cupola, and the Mill Dam Mine Company's smelter on the mine site at Hucklow.

With the greater demand for smelting facilities, and to be nearer the coal supply, the smelting sites moved further eastwards towards the Derbyshire and Yorkshire coal measures. These were far more efficient air-blown furnaces which could also process the fine ore that earlier miners had discarded as uneconomic for smelting.

In the early 19th Century there were further developments in the scale of mining operations. The traditional ways of conducting mining affairs had to make way for the new. Instead of acquiring measured meers along an individual vein these larger ventures obtained title to a compact area of ground, known in Derbyshire as a 'Consolidated Title'.

A clearer understanding of the area's geology also helped in bringing a more scientific approach to mining activities and workings could now be developed to depths exceeding 700ft. The mine workings might include mechanical winding gear, pumping and ancillary equipment and outlying shafts furnished with horse gins. Drainage could be implemented by deep level soughs, driven from a valley which might be 2 miles distant, and the underground transport systems improved with haulage gates laid with iron rails for tubs carrying mineral to the shafts where it would await lifting to the surface.

More efficient methods of mineral extraction, such as overhand stoping, began to be widely used in the larger mines. Cast steel borers replaced cast iron borers about 1837; mechanised boring drills began to appear in the 1870s.

In spite of all this innovation some ventures proved only to be expensive failures. Steam powered pumps and coal fired furnaces certainly made things more efficient, but the running costs of these were extremely expensive. They consumed vast quantities of coal which had to be transported from the coalfield of east Derbyshire and south Yorkshire.

Even the best entrepreneurs didn't always get it right. William Wyatt was regarded as one of the best in the business in the early 1800s but he managed to lose £19,000 at High Rake Mine, £20,000 at Watergrove (Wardlow Mires) and other assorted mining ventures that went wrong accounted for another £20,000. Nevertheless, he still managed to come out of it very well and was still acting as an agent for many of the best mining ventures in the area until his death in 1858.

With cheaper sources of lead being established in other parts of the world during the later 19th Century the home industry began to decline rapidly. In 1861 there were 2,333 men engaged in lead mining throughout the Derbyshire orefield, but by 1901 there were a mere 285.

It is ironic that today the most valuable commodity produced from the Derbyshire orefields is fluorspar, the mineral generally discarded by the old miners as being worthless. Although as early as 1670 there are records of its use as a flux in the smelting process at Beeley Smelting Mill. Considerable quantities have been produced in recent years from the reworking of the vein along Hucklow Edge from Mill Dam Mine to Ladywash Mine in Eyam, together with that from mines on Longstone edge and by reclamation from old surface dumps. The Peak District is one of the world's leading producers of fine grade fluorspar. Now, because the lead ore though not actively sought is a valuable by-product of the fluorspar industry, with the re-opening of Mill Dam Mine it may be said that lead mining is still practised in our parish.

Using a two-handled stowe for raising a kibble of ore from a shaft

Loading the ore at the base of a shaft (Science and Society Library)

The prints appearing on these and previous pages are reproduced by kind permission of the **Science Museum / Science & Society Picture Library**. Although the prints were made in the early 19th Century of mining activities in Northumberland, they would be very similar to those in the Derbyshire orefield.

A miner descends into the mine, with a day's supply of candles suspended on his back.

Buddling

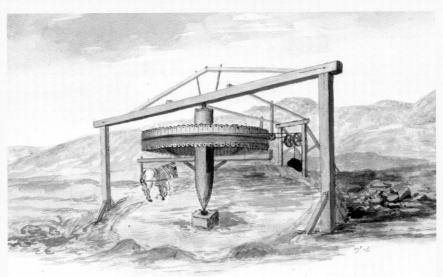

A horse gin or whimsey - a horse powered winding drum for raising mineral from the mine or lowering heavy timbers or other equipment into it.

Weighing ore and packing into sacks before transporting to the smelter by pack horse.

Dressing ore with hammer and bucking iron

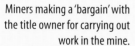

Miners making a 'bargain' with the title owner for carrying out work in the mine.

2. The Laws and Customs of Lead Mining

It took hundreds of years to establish the many laws, customs, practices and traditions of the lead miners which were driven, formed and codified by the many interested forces at work in the industry. Almost from the very beginning the Crown had a vested interest in making the winning of the lead by the miners a worthwhile proposition, realising that a flourishing mining industry would be a good source of revenue. In spite of the natural difficulties and hazards of the work the Crown saw lead as an important commodity to be assiduously sought and won.

The Crown was the titular 'owner' of all minerals beneath the ground. The 'King's Dish' was a portion due to the Crown of the value of all ore mined and was a token acknowledgment of its ownership. If mining was to flourish it was important that its customs should allow and encourage the seeking and winning of the ore, and the laws must also have the effect of protecting the miners in carrying out their work.

The customs and laws which controlled the lead industry had their origin in Anglo Saxon times and each mining area has developed its own version of the laws. In Derbyshire at an inquisition held at Ashbourne on the Saturday after Holy Trinity 1288, the sixteenth year of the reign of Edward I, the first surviving document was produced (Quo Warranto) which records some of the ancient privileges enjoyed by Derbyshire miners. Only fourteen customs were listed but during succeeding centuries other clauses were added.

These ancient rights and customs of the lead miners allowed any man, or men, to dig for lead anywhere in the Kings/Queensfield, which covered the greater part of the Derbyshire limestone area, without permission of owners or tenants of the land, or liability for damage. They could not dig, however, in churchyards, places of worship, burial grounds, dwelling houses, orchards, gardens, pleasure grounds or highways. If no lead was gained within 14 days then the land had to be levelled and left as found.

The Barmote Courts, each with its jury of miners (called the Body of the Mine), was established from very early times to oversee and enforce the laws and to settle disputes. These local courts continued to introduce new articles to allow prospecting and development of newly discovered lead veins without continual litigation while applying agreed methods to establish ownership to the title of a mine.

Miners also had the right to carry the mined ore to the nearest highway and, if the owner of the land to be crossed objected, the Barmaster was called. With two of his jurymen, one either side with arms out-stretched, the Barmaster would walk direct from the mine to the highway, driving marker pegs at the limit of the hands. The miners could carry their ore between these pegs, whether through corn or any other crop. The explanation of these apparently unfair laws is that, when they were made, most of the district would have been barren and waste. The men who bought and cultivated the land would know these laws.

Over the centuries the miners themselves built up a complex but necessary code of practice to protect and encourage their industry, and also to set down agreed procedures, such as the way that title to a mine should be established, how ore should be processed, and sold, and how appropriate penalties for those who contravened the laws and customs should be administered. Laws governing what we might today call 'health and safety' issues were fairly minimal then. This code of agreed procedures was also extended to the methods of work and the relationship between miners themselves, the mine owners, the lead merchant and smelters. As mining technology improved, geology more fully understood and commercial interest and investment became more important, the laws and practices had to be modified to take them into account, though often giving rise to much dispute and disagreement.

To complicate matters further the holders of the local mineral rights could also claim a portion of the value of the ore. Lord Cullen was one such Lord of the Manor who claimed he owned the mineral duties of the Liberty of Grindlow acquired by the Cavendish family after the dissolution of Lilleshall Abbey (see Silence Mine page 100).

However, these laws and customs had been

originally evolved in a system where the mining was done by an individual or a small group working within a carefully defined area and at no great depth. When the code had to adapt to a deeper mining system, with pumping and winding engines, drainage soughs, investment of venture capital from 'partners' and all the increase in demand from an increasingly industrial based society, then the ancient traditional ways of doing things began to creak and groan.

It was becoming clear in the early 19th Century that the Barmote Courts, as they were then constituted, were very inefficient and could no longer be the sole arbiters of the laws and customs if judgements were to be fair to all. Pressure from the 'vested interest' sections of the lead mining industry (holders of the lordships, freeholders, partners, investors in smelting and trading ventures) eventually resulted in the laws and customs of Derbyshire being formally codified in an Act of Parliament known as the 'High Peak Mining Customs and Mineral Courts Act 1851'. This meant that the higher courts of Assize could hear litigation which could not otherwise be settled at Barmote level. The Assize Courts set down strict administrative rules and regulations for Barmote Courts.

Before these Acts of Parliament the ancient mining law and customs were wonderfully encapsulated in a piece of doggerel verse known as 'Manlove', after Edward Manlove who first devised it sometime during the Commonwealth period. The work was some 300 lines long and enabled anyone with a good memory to absorb all the salient points of the mining law without the necessity of being able to read.

As a measure of the complications of mining law the Act of 1851 stretched to over 60 pages of text to cover all that was originally contained in Manlove's 300 lines. Thomas Tapping's commentary on and exposition of the Act stretches to a further 90 pages.

In his commentary Tapping is confident that the civil aspects of laws will be far easier and fairer to administer for the industry as a whole, and he is also pleased that the criminal part, or at least punishments for wrong doing, would be dealt with in a more civilised manner (fines). A particular part of Manlove which so alarmed him was:

For stealing oar twice from the minery
The Thief that's taken fined twice shall be,
But the third time, that he commits such theft
Shall have a knife stuck through his hand to th'
Haft
Into the Stow, and there till death shall stand,
Or loose himself by cuttingwrong para style –
should be QuoteParagraph_02 loose his hand
and shall foreswear the franchise of the mine
and always lose his freedom from that time.

In other words, the choice of starving to death, or drawing your pinioned hand through the blade of the knife, although it is not certain whether this barbaric punishment was ever infact carried out.

The terms Wapentake and Hundred had roughly the same meaning, ie a defined administrative part of a county; although Manlove's poem was particular to the custom and laws of the Wapentake of Wirksworth they were in essence very similar to those of the Hundred of the High Peak.

The Kings/Queensfield

The Kingsfield in Derbyshire includes two areas of jurisdiction the High Peak and the Low Peak or the Soke and Wapentake of Wirksworth in which lead rights and royalties are owned by the monarch. The Crown has held these rights since the eleventh century and probably even in Anglo Saxon times and they came to be administered for the Crown by the Duchy of Lancaster. Each area consists of a collection of Liberties which usually correspond with the parish boundary. Outside the Kingsfield the lead mining royalties are owned by individuals such as the Dukes of Devonshire and Rutland.

Since early times the lead mining royalties due to the Crown have been frequently leased to individuals on payment of an annual rent or 'farm'. Farmers therefore were lessees of the duties of 'lot and cope' (collection of mining duties payable to the Lord of the Manor and the Crown) and recipients of 'meer' dishes and freeing duties. Frequently the lessees of the farm or farmers were members of the aristocracy, landed gentry or wealthy entrepreneurs especially lead merchants who could control the output of the mines, smelting and market sales and so they effectively came to dictate the industry.

The Barmote Court

The Barmaster was and still is the executive officer of the Barmote Court appointed by the Crown in the Kingsfield or by the Lord of the Liberty.

The word 'Barmote' came originally from the Anglo-Saxon 'berg moot', (written as 'Barghmoot' in Manlove) meaning a meeting place on top of a hill where disputed matters could be discussed and decided.

A jury of miners originally (24 and later 12) assisted the Barmaster in his duties. The principle responsibilities of a Barmaster were:

'to summon the court; regularly walk through his liberty to inspect mines; and 'nick' the stows when required; attend freeing and transfers of titles; layout the meers; provide a dish for ore measurement and perform such measurement at each mine; ensure that lot and cope were collected and collect other duties such as meer dishes on behalf of the Lord of the field; layout mineral roads to the mine and to water. He assisted the jury in their deliberations when bills of complaint were proffered and arrested mines in dispute. Before the parliamentary acts of 1851 and 1852 he acted as coroner in cases of death at or in the mine'.

Disputes over the extent of ownership were settled by the Barmaster and his Jury as illustrated in the letter sent by the Barmaster Matthew Frost in 1836 informing the agent Mr Wyatt that he would attend on the 1st of June at 11 o'clock at Old Edge Mine and New Edge Mine to determine the extent of the titles.

The private liberties such as Grindlow had the power to appoint their own Barmasters where the position existed before 1288. In the bigger liberties deputy Barmasters were elected by the miners.

Freemining

Any man was allowed to prospect for lead ore within the Kingsfield without hindrance from the land-owner. The only condition was that once a miner found a lead vein he freed it according to the custom laid down by the Barmote Court. This was the system of free-mining which the landowners such as the Cavendishes and the Manners opposed so vehemently in the 17th Century, claiming that it threatened social stability and could be extended to other industries and gave rise to the protests at Little Hucklow in the late 1500s. Failing to exert any influence over the Barmote Court the gentry tried to take cases to a higher court of the Duchy of Lancaster. This court, which oversaw the Kingsfield on behalf of the Crown, protected the miners until it was abolished by the Parliamentarians but after its re-establishment in 1657 its capacity to support the miners was considerably reduced. The gentry were then able to take their cases to the Duchy Court or to the courts at Westminster, realising that very few miners could afford the costs of expensive actions at those courts, as happened in the case of Ann Turner in 1848 (see Great Hucklow Liberty, Hill Top Mine p 54).

Even as late as the 1930s freemining was still being used by the impoverished to supplement their income.

Meers, Stowes, Freeing and Nicking

Meer – was a linear measurement along a vein which varied in each area; it was measured by the Barmaster's chain which in the High Peak was 32 yards. The title (ownership) was laid out by the Barmaster's chain, and a miniature stowe, known as a possession stowe, indicated that the mine was in use and marked the extent of each meer. A meer stake or stone post was placed at each end of a mining title to show the boundary of each mine.

Stowe – was originally an apparatus for drawing up the materials and water in tubs from the mine. A possession stowe was a very small model of a stowe placed on top of a stake placed at the end of each meer, which had to be made entirely of wood and pinned with wood according to custom. If nails were used in its construction it was considered invalid as a possession marker.

Freeing – The first dish of ore obtained when a miner begins to work a meer of ground was given via the Barmaster to the owner or lessee of the mineral duties which ensured that the meer was 'freed' and could be put into lawful workmanship. The miner was then able to work through his two founder meers as deep as he was able and as wide as the width of the vein. He could then work through the third meer which was called the Lord's meer and belonged to the owner or lessee of the mineral duties to his 'taker' meers that is the meers beyond the two founder meers and the Lord's meer, provided he did not sell any of the ore gained from the Lord's meer. Alternatively the miner could buy the Lord's meer outright. After this the miner was allowed to free as many of his taker meers as he wanted. Each taker meer was similarly freed by giving the first dish of ore to the Barmaster. The procedure was similar each time the vein was reworked as an old vein or old mine except that the miner only had to work through one Founder meer and no Lord's meer When a miner came to a break vein or branch vein and was unsure which of the two were the continuation of his main vein to ensure his title could not be forfeited to the Lord of the field he double-freed by giving two dishes of ore to the Barmaster.

Individual miners were allowed to claim meers provided they paid their 'freeing dishes' and in return for this and other privileges the miners were charged various duties or royalties such as 'lot 'and 'cope'. Normally in the Kingsfield 'Lot' was 1/13 of the ore mined which was payable to the Mineral Lord and the duty was certainly in existence in the 13th Century. 'Cope' of about 4d per load was usually paid by the lead merchants in lieu of the Crown or its Lessee having the first

right to purchase the ore. The miner was therefore generally independent or 'free' and virtually self employed, provided he paid his dues, until the time of the large companies of the 19th Century. It is not surprising that the Barmaster had to inspect each mine regularly to ensure that the miners adhered to this seemingly complicated system.

Nicking – A mine or meer of ground lying un-worked and deserted could be claimed by another miner and put into workmanship by nicking or scoring the spindle of the stowe. This established the right to work the mine in the hope of producing sufficient ore before the spindle was nicked for the third time by the Barmaster in order to claim the title: 'Any meer standing unwrought 3 weeks together, he (the Barmaster) shall score three scores on the Spindle, and deliver it to him that will work it' (Old Customary c1500).

After the acts of parliament of 1851 and 1852 forfeiture of an abandoned mine relied on the posting of notices on the mine and to the mine owner, except, as at Bradwell and elsewhere where the ancient practice continued as a custom but did not carry legal significance

Transfer of mining title at a stowe above a shaft on Moss Rake, Bradwell, 1906.

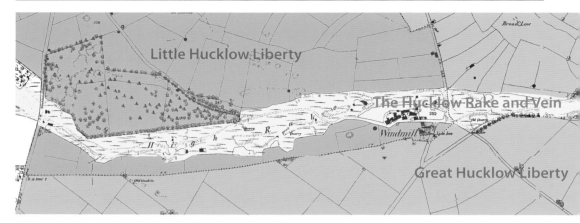

3. An Overview of the Hucklow Mines

In this section we sketch the background to the lead mines on the Hucklow Edge in what is now the modern parish of Great Hucklow – to give details of every known shaft and mine there has ever been in the parish would be beyond the expertise of this book, even if it were possible to do so. Just as hundreds of generations have mined these few hundreds of acres there are equally hundreds of mining enterprises that have left their mark on the landscape, some of which we still have evidence for, and of the title names they were given, whilst most others have long passed into obscurity. While all known shafts have been capped many must still lie undetected and could fall in at any time. For this reason we advise those interested in tracing the mines to keep to well worn footpaths.

The modern civil parish of Great Hucklow is an amalgamation of three earlier parishes - those of Great Hucklow, Little Hucklow and Grindlow, all of which were once part of the enormous ecclesiastical parish of Hope. Today, the area looks 'of a piece', but the earlier boundaries were very important and significant to the lead miners, and particularly important were the ancient manor or parish boundaries which usually corresponded to those of the lead Liberties as these carried with them many rights and privileges particularly pertaining to the mining of minerals.

Even In the mid 1850s the three manors still had their 'lords' and 'ladies' – the Lord of the Manor of Great Hucklow was Mr Andrew Brittlebank, that of Little Hucklow was a Captain William Carlyle, and the holder of the Grindlow manorial rights was a Mrs Wake. However, Great Hucklow and Little Hucklow lead mining rights were under the jurisdiction of the Kingsfield but the lord of the field of Grindlow was the Lord of the Manor, which had a significant effect on the history of the Grindlow mines.

We have very little written evidence for the mines on the Hucklow Edge Vein until the late 1600s except for records or documents which happen to survive of the many court cases in the Barmote Court or the Court of the Duchy of Lancaster. Before this time, much of the mining was done by small groups of men or even individuals who were unlikely to be able to write. It is really in the 1600s when lead mining became very profitable that the more educated became involved as owners or shareholders and later agents. From then on we are fortunate to have some written evidence either from family papers such as the Bagshawe Collection, to which we are indebted for much of our information, the Shuttleworth family papers and the Devonshire Collection. For the years from Anglo Saxon times to the 1600s we have to rely on what can be gleaned from surface observation and archaeology with occasional records of the number of loads of lead ore produced in an area or any assumptions drawn from other historical evidence.

The earliest mines followed the mineral veins or rakes from the surface. The 'V' shaped ditches on Tideslow are indicative of open cast mining from possibly 1200s or even earlier but there are several shafts among them which later miners must have dug as the surface ore began to run out.

Tideslow is also remarkable in that it can boast

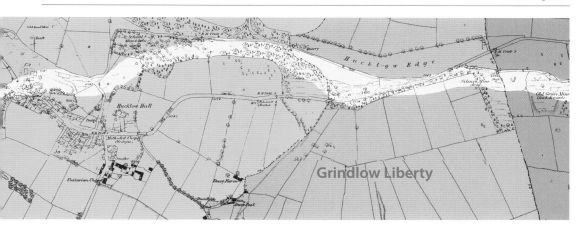

Grindlow Liberty

one of the earliest soughs (drainage tunnel) which was begun in 1654 and was nearly half a mile in length by the winter of 1685. Its necessity indicates that the level of the mine must have been driven below the water table and that already 'adventurers', as shareholders were known, were willing to invest large sums of money.

The Little Hucklow Liberty

It is difficult to imagine that at the close of the reign of Elizabeth I Little Hucklow Liberty was a centre of political activity in Derbyshire with the free miners banding together to protect their long established mining rights from the wealthy families such as the Foljambes of Chesterfield and the Manners of Haddon, who in turn held the manorial rights. Both sides were keen to exploit the increase in demand for lead.

The first documented evidence of unrest in the Little Hucklow Liberty appears in 1597 when John Burton of Tideswell defended the Little Hucklow miners' right to free mining at the Barmote Court. Another miners' dispute arose in Little Hucklow, 1612-1613, involving fifty miners from the surrounding area over their rights to 'free mining' (see chapter on Laws and Customs p 16). Between 1619 and1622 the Duchy Court eventually guaranteed the rights of free mining within the manors of Little Hucklow and Great Hucklow. The organisation and determination of the miners in the early 1600s was remarkable given that they could successfully challenge the wealthy families.

The mining activity on the TideslowRake before the 1600s must have extended into the Little Hucklow Liberty. The scene would have been one of small groups of hopeful miners or individuals, all digging along the rake for the lead ore close to the surface. They had a good eye for the terrain and knew where the vein and its offshoots were likely to be.

The western end of the rake which has been planted with trees was originally covered with spoil heaps. These were reworked in the twentieth century to reclaim the minerals discarded by the early miners (known locally as hillocking) and then used for a time as a rubbish dump. The land was then bought by the Peak District National Park who planted it with trees. Most of the activity therefore of the earlier miners with the exception of High Rake mine was obliterated. The area to the east of the trees nearer to Windmill resembles Tideslow and may well be evidence of open cast mining well before the eighteenth century. There are large hollows here which may contain shafts obscured by the later hillocking and the area should not be explored.

Along the rake in the Little Hucklow Liberty the limestone is very 'shakey' and allows for drainage through self openings or swallows in the limestone –an important consideration before efficient pumps were devised and soughs were difficult and slow to drive and very expensive. In the last half of the 19th Century the miners of Little Hucklow, driving ever deeper, unexpectedly encountered below the limestone a layer of toadstone, a Derbyshire name for a type of dense igneous rock containing no ore. In some places this was not too thick but in the case of High Rake so thick that it led to disastrous results.

The Great Hucklow Liberty

From our evidence there was a significant difference between the early mining activity of the two Hucklow Liberties in part due to their geological nature. The shale only begins to cover the limestone at Mill Dam in the Great Hucklow Liberty and becomes increasingly thicker further to the east. This meant that initially the lead bearing veins were easier to reach for the early free miners in the Little Hucklow Liberty and the western end of the Great Hucklow Liberty.

In both Liberties the miners had the right to free mining under the jurisdiction of the Kingsfield but before the nineteenth century the independent or free miner was more active in the area where the ore was nearer the surface. To reach the ore beneath the shale, shafts and levels had to be driven into the hillside incurring considerable expense before any profit could be made. From the beginning of the eighteenth century therefore the mines east of Mill Dam Mine were developed by the families of the landed gentry such as the Bagshaws and Ashtons/Spencers who had the capital to invest in the mines. By the nineteenth century the free miners of both Liberties lacked the resources to exploit the new technology and provide sufficient drainage once the upper parts of the veins had been exhausted, Many miners therefore had little option but to become a coper, one of a gang of labourers who to had to 'bargain' for work every six or seven weeks and work for a larger consortium of shareholders, as at High Rake or Mill Dam Mine.

The line of the Bradwell Road divides the two Liberties of Little Hucklow and Great Hucklow. The land on the south side of the Rake Road which leads to Great Hucklow is bounded by a limestone outcrop and has been cleared of hillocks so the usual surface evidence which indicates mining activity is absent. The clearance, however, did reveal the principal shafts of Hill Top and Beech Grove Mines and Gateside Mine. We know that Hilltop mine was worked from the beginning of the 1600s since coins dating from 1605-1680, have been found down the mine as well as tools dating from this period.The toadstone was not such a problem in this section of the vein except for Hill Top Mine, part of The Great Hucklow Mining Co. The company sank a shaft that reached the toadstone at about 453 feet. They continued to sink through the toadstone to about 600 feet before being forced to close the mine in 1873.

At Mill Dam Mine the miners encountered the Edale shale which covered the limestone in varying depths throughout the rest of the vein to the Eyam Liberty. This had to be penetrated by shafts or levels cut into the hillside before the miners could reach the lead veins in the limestone. Mill Dam became an important mine from about 1850-1880 and some interesting surface evidence still exists.

Old Edge Grove Mine to the east of Mill Dam Mine, in what is now Hucklow Woods, was one of the most important mines in Derbyshire in the 1600s and the wealth of Old Edge and New Edge mine attracted lengthy lawsuits in the Barmote Court and even in the court of the Duchy of Lancaster between 1695-1710. This area must therefore have been a hive of activity well before the 1700s. The hillocks throughout the woods bear witness to at least five mines along the rake.

Grindlow Liberty

The border between the Great Hucklow and Grindlow Liberties crosses the Bretton Road shortly before the Abney Road junction. Here Speed Grove and Bank Grove Mines were situated but there is little surface evidence. Silence Mine on the other hand which is to be found near the entrance to the newly created 'Silence Heritage Site' is being excavated by the Peak District Mines Historical Society who began work in May 2008. Further to the east along the Heritage Site path is Old Grove Mine. Silence Mine is significant in many respects but especially for the involvement of its miners in the Grindlow Riot of 1738.

In 1199 Grindlow was granted to Lilleshaw Abbey in Shropshire as a Grange which was a parcel of land and buildings belonging to a religious house or order and used as a source of food and finance. It became a Customary Lordship and the Crown ceased to be in control of the land and its mineral rights.

Further details of the reasons for this and the extraordinary armed confrontation which ensued from the mineral disputes can be found in the chapter on the The Grindlow Liberty.

Artis Farm and its Leadmining Heritage

The story of Artis Farm, its land and its inhabitants, is a good illustration of the pattern of lead mining in the Great Hucklow Liberty over 300 years. The present building dates from the early 1600s and is one of the oldest in Great Hucklow, a substantial building for its period.

The farm lies just south of the Hucklow Edge Vein on the western side of the village. In the seventeenth century farmers were keen to exploit the rich pickings to be had from the lead on their land as long as the ore was close to the surface and relatively easy to obtain. There must have been many shafts in the 1600s belonging to free miners on the vein south of the rake road leading to Windmill. The present owner of the farm, Mr. Kenneth Waterhouse, has inadvertently come upon the shafts of several of these in the course of his farming. Free miners had the right to prospect for ore on any land in the Kingsfield regardless of who owned it provided they fulfilled the custom laid down by the Barmote Court.

Mr. Waterhouse gathers from his deeds for the farm that the owners in the 1600s lived in the house and, he assumes, mined as much lead ore as the family could. To support this theory, Hext Mine which was close to the house, appears to have been a drift mine typical of early mining ventures. There is a record of a Bill of Complaint at the Great Barmote Court in 1730 against the partners of Hext mine for non-payment of bills. Mr. Waterhouse thinks it is significant that it is soon after this that the family leave the farm and rent out the house and land. This is at a time when the price for lead was falling. Most of the accessible ore had been exhausted and greater investment in

sinking deeper shafts and driving drainage soughs had become necessary. Conditions for the free miner became very tough and many therefore were either forced to sell up or join a consortium and look for investors. Many of the mine names disappeared from the records and their miners often ended up as copers, or contract miners for the larger concerns. By the 1800s the consolidated mines on the farm's land were Hill Top, Beech Grove and Gateside. In the 1841 census four of the Wilson family who were living at Artis farm were lead miners but we do not know in which mine they worked.

Mr Waterhouse's great great grandfather William came to Great Hucklow from Ashford in the 1830s as a trained blacksmith to work for the mines, living at first in a cottage near the Queen's Head Inn (now the Queen Anne). At this time new technology had led to a resurgence in men prepared to invest in lead mining. William Waterhouse appears in the 1841 census aged 30 with two sons Joshua (8) and Joseph (6). He worked for Mill Dam Mine which together with Gateside mine became The Mill Dam Mining Company in the 1850s. In the 1861 census William had produced two further sons Benjamin and William and he was still a blacksmith, His two older sons were lead miners (see Gorse Bush Mine). Mr Waterhouse's great grandfather, William, the youngest son continued in the role of blacksmith at the smithy at Mill Dam Mine. Blacksmiths had a very important role in lead mining, making and repairing the tools and machinery.

By the 1891 census the affect of the mine closures on employment is clear. The two older Waterhouse sons were no longer lead miners, Joshua was a

Artis Farm, Great Hucklow

farmer at Stanley House and Joseph who had been a farmer and lead miner at Windmill had moved to Stockport and become a greengrocer. Benjamin was a carpenter and farmer living in Sycamore House, as it is now known. He later worked in the quarries while still farming. William was now a farmer as well as blacksmith.

Today the area along the rake has been cleared of hillocks and the peaceful scene gives little indication of the mining activity over 300 years. Mr Kenneth Waterhouse farms this land and is one of the few residents of Great Hucklow left who have heard first hand accounts from those actually involved in the gaining of the ore.

Owners, Agents, Smelters and Bankers

The Landed Lead Merchant versus the Free Miner

In 1590 large scale possession of land was not essential to accumulate wealth in Derbyshire. Anyone was entitled to dig for lead in the Kingsfield provided he 'freed' his mine and paid his dues. A greater proportion of the population were classed as freeholders than elsewhere and at least 200 families possessed sufficient wealth to rank as country gentry with gentlemen and yeomen beneath them. A small nucleus of about twenty-five families who headed the gentry supplemented their wealth as farmers and landlords with the exploitation of lead, operating smelting mills and selling the finished product – among these were the Cavendish and Manners families. A conflict thus arose between the free miners of the Kingsfield and these wealthy men who attempted as lords of the manor to exact royalties from the miners and force them to sell their ore to them at a fixed price. The protest of 1612-1613 at Little Hucklow involving fifty miners is an excellent example of a successful rebellion of the independent or free miner against the Cavendish and Manners monopoly which resulted in the Court of the Duchy of Lancaster guaranteeing the right to free mining in the manors of Great and Little Hucklow and extended the Kingsfield into these manors.

The Bagshaw family: from yeoman to gentleman

The Bagshaw family were among the leading figures in the mining industry on Hucklow and Eyam Edges in the 17th and 18th Centuries. An ancient Derbyshire family, they were already playing a major role in 1634 before the Civil War 1642-49. From their history we can learn much about how lead was exploited and financed by the new landed class.

Many cases were brought by the lesser gentry to the Barmote Court against the dominant wealthy families. In 1634 William Bagshaw, yeoman of Litton, became involved in the resistance to these powerful families. After the Reformation in some parts of Derbyshire a tithe of every tenth dish of lead which had previously been paid to the Church had to be paid to the Crown in addition to the royalties of 'lot and cope'.

At this time the tithe was very valuable and in 1631 the right to collect tithes in the High Peak was sold to the Dowager Countess of Devonshire. The miners had also tried to purchase the tithe. In 1634 a 'mutinous' petition was presented to the Lord Lieutenant of Derbyshire, the Earl of Newcastle, by the miners. The four miners' leaders were arrested and taken to Derby gaol, among them William Bagshaw, yeoman of Litton, who was organiser of the petition; however, one observer is recorded as saying 'almost 20 who pretended themselves miners are wealthy and sufficient freeholders'. He was right; William Bagshaw possessed a small holding with several cottages and years later his estate was valued at over £5000. This was the man who bought Hucklow Hall and estate for £433..6s..8d and by then had earned the title of 'gentleman'. His father-in-law, Ralphe Oldfield of Litton, was likewise a miners' leader, and they were typical of an articulate class who were able to represent the wider discontent of the miners.

The tithe question might have been settled at the beginning of the Civil War when the Devonshires agreed with the assent of Charles I to exempt the miners from payment of the tithe in return for the support of the royalist cause. Charles II and his Restoration government, however, did not honour his father's promise and the miners of the parishes of Hope, Bakewell and Tideswell continued to pay their tithes with little interruption.

The rapid expansion of the lead industry in the 17th Century meant that by 1642 as many as 20,000 men, women and children were involved in the High Peak and Wirksworth Kingsfields but in spite of the many protests fewer than 2,000 were independent or free miners; the rest were hired labourers or workmen in associated trades. There were rich rewards to be had for the gentleman 'farmer' or 'adventurer' from investing in the mines at this time.

The Bagshaw Family and their connection with Hucklow

Many of the descendents of the Bagshaw family, achieved the status of 'gentleman,' several of them becoming involved in the lead business. The family records in the Bagshawe papers in the John Rylands Library in Manchester and the Sheffield Archive Library deserve a book of their own.

Initially William Bagshaw of Litton, the champion of miners' rights in 1634 and Barmaster of Tideswell in 1638, identified with the yeoman class, and as a Presbyterian became a supporter of the Parliamentarians. He began to prosper during the Commonwealth government of Oliver Cromwell, by buying up sequestered land and titles belonging to Royalists. By 1650 William had acquired the title of gentleman and in 1654 bought the manor of Great Hucklow and the Hall.

In 1657 he bought the lead tithes of Tideswell and Litton so that he came to collect the very tithes to which he had led the free miners' opposition in 1634. He became even more unpopular with the miners when he enclosed the common fields in Great Hucklow. Moreover in 1657 he secured the forfeited lands in Hucklow of William Cavendish, Earl of Newcastle for £2,400. It was possibly part of this land that he and his descendants were able to claim as 'decreed' or 'free' land.

His son John became High Sheriff and inherited the Lordship of Great Hucklow with the right of lot and cope and lived in Hucklow Hall. His other son William became known as the Apostle of the Peak and he founded a Presbyterian congregation in 1696 at Grindlow. This became one of the first Unitarian congregations which was eventually responsible for building in 1796 what is now known as the Old Chapel in Great Hucklow.

William Bagshaw senior had bought Ford Hall near Chapel-en-Frith for £1300 in 1662/3 and settled it on his son William, the Apostle, in his will although William was already living there.

Other members of the family came to own Oakes at Norton, Sheffield, Bagshaw Hall in Bakewell and Bagshaw Hall at Wormhill where a branch of the family still live. A Reverend William Bagshaw was vicar of Wormhill, but clearly retained his lead mining interests judging from his correspondence between 1813 and 1843. There was also a branch at Castleton, notably Richard Bagshaw, who was active in the mining industry. The Bagshaw mines at Eyam, where the family were particularly involved, and the Bagshaw Cavern at Bradwell are reminders of their influence locally.

The Bagshaw family continued to play an important part in the mining industry in the Hucklow area. In 1725 the imposing New Hall, now known as the Old Manse, was built in the centre of Great Hucklow probably by a Bagshaw. The family intermarried with several of the families involved in lead. Aymer Rich, who belonged to a dissenting family from Bullhouse, near Penistone and derived his wealth from the cloth industry, became heavily involved in lead after his marriage in 1722 to Grace, daughter of John Bagshaw. His heiress was his niece Mary Rhodes and after her, her sister, Martha Buske. When Martha's daughter Rachel died the estate was sold in 1805 and the line of inheritance from William Bagshaw was finally broken. The Hucklow estate was sold to solicitors Rimington and Wake; Mrs Bernard Wake came to own the manorial rights and Hucklow Hall but probably never lived in it and sold it in 1921 to Mr Arthur Maltby. The Hall had been leased out to Arthur's father, Leonard, since 1881 and before him to several other tenants.

The spelling of the family name varies over the years so we have decided to use the 'Bagshaw' variant without the final 'e' where possible.

Ralphe Oldfield and family

Ralphe Oldfield of Litton was an important figure in the early 17th Century in the area around the Great and Little Hucklows. He was a free miner and minor landholder and his daughter Jane married William Bagshaw in 1625.

The miners of the two Hucklows were much poorer than those of Tideswell. Landless and dependent on a wage they were forced to pay the lead tithes demanded by the Lords of the Manor. The more independent miners from neighbouring parishes such as John Burton (see Overview, Little Hucklow Liberty) and Ralphe Oldfield from Tideswell supported them in their resistance to the demands of the Lords of the Manor.

In 1613 Ralphe Oldfield was instrumental in extending the free mining rights of the Kingsfield into the two manors of Great and Little Hucklow. For thirty years he was one of the leaders of the movement to abolish the tithes and to establish rights to free mining. He was very well versed in all mining law and renowned for knowing the mining customs of the High Peak by heart; a useful asset since the first printed version of the mining customs was only produced in 1645. Oldfield appeared in many court cases for the miners leading the resistance to the payment of lead tithes and enclosures of common land. In 1634 he was imprisoned along with William Bagshaw, his son in law, for being one of the leaders of the demonstration against the payment of tithes. Unlike William he remained true to the cause of the free miner throughout his life. A number of his sons continued his work defending the free miners and the name of Oldfield appears in documents relating to various mines in the area well into the nineteenth century.

The Maltby family

Leonard Maltby, born 1825, came to Great Hucklow as mine manager at Mill Dam Mine in about 1870 when he married Mary Bagshaw from Great Hucklow. Which of the many Bagshaw families Mary belonged to is difficult to tell without more research but it was not that of the original John Bagshaw of Hucklow Hall. In 1881 Leonard and Mary moved into the Hall. Arthur, Leonard's son, continued to live in the Hall and bought it in 1921 along with a large tract of land from Mrs B. Wake which included many of the mines on the vein in Great Hucklow. He married Roberta Lucy Ash of Great Hucklow, daughter of Robert and Sarah Ash a mining family, and in turn had a son Leonard whom many people still living in the village can remember; he continued to live in the Hall until four years before his death in 1981. There was a mine known as Maltby's

Venture in the area of the Rake road but little is known about it. However, the very name indicates that one of Leonard's forebears must have been a mine owner.

Mary Jane, daughter of Leonard senior and Mary Maltby, married James Furness of Cartledge House, and the Furness family still farm at Cartledge House today.

The Ash family

The Ash family are recorded as leadminers as well as farmers in various directories and census returns of the nineteenth century. Some lived in Great Hucklow in the houses known even today as Ash Cottage and Ash House which still has its croft but no cow or pig. In 1841 Benjamin Ash, aged 40, is listed as Leadminer and Thomas and Francis, aged 50 and 40 respectively, as Farmer and Leadminer. Francis is still referred to as leadminer in 1857 but in 1861 he is only listed as farmer of 11 acres. Francis Ash was joint owner of Smithy Coe Mine when the Mill Dam Mining Company acquired the lease of that part of the mine below 300 feet in the 1850s and in a letter of 1859 from John AS Shuttleworth he is again listed as one of the proprietors along with John Frost, George Walker and Benjamin Walker. At this time the upper part of Smithy Coe Mine above 300 feet would have been largely exhausted while perversely the lower section mined by Mill Dam Mine between 1868 and 1878 produced large amounts of lead ore; however, the owners would have benefited from the lease to Mill Dam Mine. By 1891 Sarah, widow of Robert, is listed as a farmer and apart from her children she is the only Ash recorded. The family must be typical of leadminers in this area supplementing their meagre incomes with lead mining but not having the capital to compete with likes of the Bagshaws and Shuttleworths. The miner would often continue to invest and work in those mines, in which the wealthier families had little interest, hoping for a small return. Many other families were in a similar position such as the Oldfields, the Needhams, Frosts and Walkers.

The Shuttleworth Family

Another family whose name appears frequently in documents is that of the Ashton/Spencer/ Shuttleworth family whose descendants still live in Hathersage. The Ashtons originally lived in Stoney Middleton Hall but Squire Ashton moved to Hathersage Hall in the early 1700s. The family then married into the Spencer family of Cannon Hall and subsequently when the succession went through the female line the family gained the surname Shuttleworth. They moved in the Nineteenth century to their present house, Nether Hall in Hathersage, on the banks of the River Derwent. There is a reference to Ashton in the Bagshawe Collection saying that the 'Hucklow Edge forefield was in possession of Ashton from October 1697 to 1701'. Squire Ashton seems to have been a colourful figure and his son Benjamin likewise who appears in a song about lead mining on the back of a document dated 1746 *'Brave Squire Ashton hath honour won Above all in Derbyshire . . . . he nobly Have At All pursues'* (see inside front cover). The song seems to imply that the miners are grateful for the employment

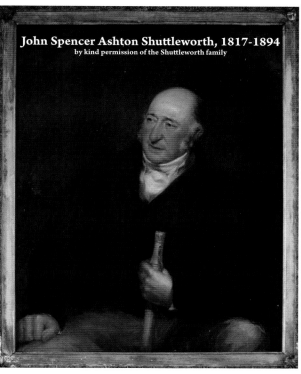

John Spencer Ashton Shuttleworth, 1817-1894
by kind permission of the Shuttleworth family

he is providing for them. Similarly in 1733 they are clearly prepared to pay tithes rather than risk losing their livelihood when Benjamin Ashton supported renewed demands for a standardised lead tithe across the whole of the lead field, a move which had been defeated in 1703 by the opposition of the free miners. The free miners on his land at Stoney Middleton, most of whom seem to have worked for him in other capacities, 'were afraid of disobliging him and being turned out of his business'.

The log books of John Spencer Ashton Shuttleworth 1817-1894 provide us with a picture of the final stages of lead mining on the Hucklow Edge and the lean time for shareholders and miners. He was only thirteen when he inherited his father's estate and mineral interests, so his guardian James Holworthy of Brookfield Manor, Hathersage, had the task in 1836 of preventing New Edge Mine, in which John Shuttleworth had 10/24 shares, from being 'nicked'.

By the mid 19th Century he has the title of New Edge, Have at All and Gorse Bush mines. Moreover, he was still referred to in Kelly's Directory of 1881 as 'Proprietor' of New Edge mine and in 1891 of Have At All mine. The death in 1858 of William

Wyatt, his agent, seems to have caused him some concern and trouble and he was clearly assiduous in sorting out his various mining interests as his letter written to Mr Thomas Bagshaw on Boxing Day, of all days, 1859, illustrates:

> 'I shall feel obliged if you will search for all documents . . . relating to Have At All Mine which were in the possession of the late Mr William Wyatt as agent . . . and deliver the same to me.'

There are several letters to various Barmasters to ascertain to which mines he had the title and descriptions of his tours of his mineral interests with Robert Howe whom he appointed as his agent. His interest too must have extended to mining affairs generally judging from his note book and collection of numerous newspaper cuttings on cases to do with mines in the High Peak. The family was involved in lead mining throughout the Hucklow Edge Vein from Cow Pasture to Mill Dam Mine and on to Ladywash at Eyam and Watergrove in Middleton Dale, their name occurring in many documents. In 1859 he was already a shareholder in the new venture at Mill Dam Mine and was appalled that no balance sheet was presented to the shareholders at the General Meeting.

Unfortunately for John SA Shuttleworth and many other shareholders investment in lead mining in the second half of the 19th Century brought poor returns, even in Mill Dam Mine. According to his family, John Shuttleworth maintained that it was the worst thing he did to allow Lord Houghton to encourage him to become involved in lead mining.

The Agents and their Clients

Before the 18th Century many of the mines would have begun as small ventures of one or two men or a family, but by the end of the 17th Century, when it became clear that there were rich pickings to be had, many adventurers were ready to invest their money in a mine provided others did the hard work.

Most of the bigger mines had several shareholders, much as would happen today. Even at the beginning of the 18th Century it was usual for investors to spread their risk among several mines. The shares were divided into twenty four parts and these frequently became subdivided. It was not uncommon to hold a share of 1/192 and some were even smaller subdivisions. In fact it seems to have been quite difficult to find out who were the shareholders of various mines. During the late 18th Century it became common for a mine agent to manage the business affairs of the mine for the shareholders. There is interesting correspondence in 1793 between Messrs Wyatt and John Bagshaw replying to a letter of his asking who the shareholders were at Ladywash Mine, of which John Bagshaw may have owned the title. Messrs Wyatt names three of the partners and says they would try and find out the names of the remainder of shareholders:

'because they thought it improper to ask themselves since the partners may regard this as interference'

and again in 1792 Messrs Wyatt writes on 5th of May to Bagshaw in connection with a mineral meeting to be held at the Bulls Head in Eyam about the reckoning of Stoke Sough and various Eyam mines:

'I can get you an account of some of the partners but these are such old mines and shares have been divided by family over and over again until they are becoming small and the partners very numerous and I believe it is not possible to get an

exact account of all the partners. I know the people who pay for all the shares at every mine whether you would think it right for me to ask them in your name whose shares they are that they pay for, some of them will tell me and some will not.'

Here part of the issue appears to be who should pay up when shareholders were called to pay in the event of a loss. Another letter sent by William Wyatt to William Bagshaw when he asked who was the largest shareholder in Miner's Engine Mine replied that it was William Bagshaw himself! No wonder it became necessary to employ agents.

Reckonings or accounts were sometimes presented every six or seven weeks when the ore had been measured and sold. The profits and losses were declared and if you were lucky the profits would be paid out or, as seemed more usual, 'calls' were paid in and creditors settled. Reading the various reckonings you frequently see that the share holders were having to pay out considerable sums during the course of the year to help balance the books; this was especially so at some of the bigger mines in the nineteenth century such as Mill Dam and High Rake.

If the shareholder did not pay up what was due, he could either 'turn up' his shares which the agents would transfer to another client or to the other partners or, if the agents thought they might profit in the future, to themselves. If the shareholders' 'friends' were either unable or unwilling to pay their losses then the ultimate resort was for the agents to apply to the Barmote Court for forfeiture to themselves not just of the shares of a particular mine but of all the mineral interests owned by the shareholder. It was in the agent's interest to try to avoid this measure and to be as helpful as possible in order to inspire confidence in their work. However, although there were times when the shares paid good dividends it seems it was pretty risky to invest in the mines themselves and one is left wondering why so many did so. But then, why do so many play the Stock Market today? The real profits were to be made in smelting which is why several of the agents had shares in the local smelting mills.

Most shareholders with a sizeable portfolio were prepared to let the agent negotiate the price of the ore with the lead merchant (who was most probably the agent himself) and organise the smelting of the lead at a mill in which the agent also had shares. However, some clients negotiated with the agent a scale of prices depending on the weight of a dish of ore and the price of lead at Hull (the port from which it was usually distributed). By the end of the 18th Century an agent would usually be responsible for all the ore from a mine.

Benjamin Wyatt, a mine agent and father of William Wyatt who expanded the business, must have found Major Roger Ashton Shuttleworth very irritating since he insisted in 1821 on having his own share of ore from Little Pasture Mine in the Eyam Liberty smelted separately from the rest of the ore. Such a small-scale operation really belonged to the previous century, but Shuttleworth liked to be a hands-on shareholder and according to Lynn Willies his 'parsimonious attitude and insistence on small scale methods was symptomatic of all that was wrong on Eyam edge.' (article in PDMHS Bulletin Vol 8 No. 6)

As well as managing the finance of the mine the agent would also be responsible for hiring the work force. A 'bargain day' would be set every six or eight weeks when teams of miners known as copers would bid for various tasks in the mine and the lowest bid was usually accepted.

William Wyatt: mine agent

William Wyatt of Foolow, cousin of the Bagshaws, (1803-1858) was an entrepreneur and social climber. He and his brother Robert farmed at Foolow but according to an 1846 directory William lived in 'a good mansion nearly opposite the church' in Eyam, and according to the census for 1851 he had two female servants and a part-time groom, so one supposes his house also had stables. Not only was he a lead merchant, agent and smelter but he owned 300 acres of farm land.

His grandfather William Wyatt, of Eyam, had founded a mine agency business and his father Benjamin had formed a partnership with Barkers, a leading firm of mine agents. By 1829 William had acquired both Barker's and his father's business. At the age of 21 (1824) he was already an agent for several mines and from the Bagshaw papers seems to have become the agent for many of those along the Hucklow Edge. He was a solicitor, mineral agent and owner of lead mining interests himself, and once he acquired the Barkers' business he

inevitably became involved in smelting as well. He made and eventually lost a fortune in the mines; over £20,000 at High Rake and likewise at Watergrove near Foolow. In all Lynn Willies (ibid) has calculated that his gross loss for the mines for which he was agent and was a major shareholder was £72,600 (in 2007 almost £54,000,000) to which could be added a further £37,900 of losses from other mines in which he had shares. Willies thinks that the profit he obtained from the ore smelted from these mines would not have made up for his personal losses. These he concludes he must have made up from his fees as agent, and on reports, on profits made from bought ore and on lead dealing and especially after 1845 on his farming and property interests. As at High Rake mine, Wyatt was reluctant to admit defeat and most closures were forced on him by the other shareholders. Tenacity was characteristic of miners: 'When you find t' cow's tail hang on 'til you find t'cow!'

Although many of Wyatt's ventures had finally to be aborted he seems to have retained the respect of shareholders and miners alike who regarded the ventures as fair risks. Moreover Lynn Willies (ibid) thinks that many of his smaller ventures were mainly to provide employment for miners driven out of work when mines had been forced to close. The steady decline in profits in the nineteenth century can largely be attributed to foreign competition and probably to the exhaustion of the veins above the toadstone. It is difficult, however, for us with the benefit of hindsight to understand the appetite for many of the ventures which ended in such losses.

The Smelters

The ore had to be 'dressed' before it was sent to the smelters and sorted for quality. The technique for dressing the ore was much the same for the 17th and 18th Centuries. 'Bing' was large lumps of pure galena (lead) and 'Bouse' lesser quality. The ore was crushed by a small flat headed iron hammer beaten on a 'knock stone' The grades were 'peasy ore' 'knock-bark' ore and a fine grained powder called 'smitham' which was then 'buddled'. The even finer particles known as 'belland' were finally able to be smelted when an improved technique was introduced in 1737 and so the buddling operations became more refined. The new process was the cupola furnace or low arched reverberatory furnace. It appears to have been made in Derbyshire concurrently but independently by the Bagshaws and the London Lead Company which was originally founded by the Quakers. The furnace was fired by coal, the flames were drawn into the ore department by the draught provided by long flues and a high chimney.

By 1780 all the ore hearths had been superseded. The Lord's Cupola in Stoney Middleton Dale, situated where the garage is now, is one of the most famous cupolas; William Wyatt came to manage it and was responsible for its rebuilding in the early 1830s. The smoke from the

The cupola smelting house in Middleton Dale *(Science and Society Library)*

processing must have been unpleasantly thick and very unhealthy confined as it was by the steep sides of the Dale. Another smelter was operating on Bretton Edge (Bird's Cupola) and after 1872 one next door to Mill Dam Mine in Great Hucklow. The court case concerning the latter smelter (Mill Dam Mine p70) reveals just how damaging to health these must have been.

It was the smelters who really made the money out of lead so it is no surprise that many of the key figures in the lead mines also had shares in smelting. In fact the mines appear to have been worked to provide raw material for the lead smelters who made a large profit on the sale of the lead.

The Bankers

In the Bagshaw and Shuttleworth collections there are accounts (from 1749 to 1758) much like a modern financial statement showing the amount of ore raised from each mine in which they had shares. Interestingly the Bagshaw accounts were sent from a firm of lead smelters, William Barker and Wilkinson, who presumably handled all the ore produced from these mines. There is also some interesting correspondence between Messrs Isaac and John Wilkinson (1790 –1801) and John Bagshaw. The Wilkinsons agreed to be the bankers for the Bagshaws, and at this time John Bagshaw

was in some financial difficulties. In reply to a letter from Bagshaw voicing his concern and apparently asking how much he can expect from his shares in Odin Mine at Castleton, Wilkinson writes on 19th Sept 1793:

"The price of lead at Hull (from where it was shipped) has always been the rule for fixing prices of ore in Derbyshire'.

He confirms that the price from Lady Day until midsummer was 35/- a load of ore and £19 per fodder of smelted ore at Hull and adds, 'but as we mentioned before there has been no selling for some time past'. It seems the smelters and the Bagshaw's bankers were making a good profit from whatever was sold at Hull. J Lawson writes,

'From many sources it seems that much of the lead mining in Derbyshire was unprofitable and it may be that the mines were worked in order to provide raw materials for the smelter (who in many cases held or paid for the majority of the shares in the mines). Perhaps the large profit which was made on the subsequent sale of the lead more than compensated the smelter at the production stage. The mines were obviously being financed by the smelters and the price was set at Hull which then set the price the smelters would give the miners.' (PDMHS Bulletin Vol 4)

4. Little Hucklow Liberty

by Sheila Martin

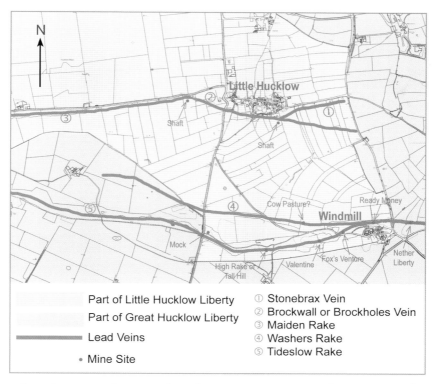

Part of Little Hucklow Liberty	① Stonebrax Vein
Part of Great Hucklow Liberty	② Brockwall or Brockholes Vein
Lead Veins	③ Maiden Rake
• Mine Site	④ Washers Rake
	⑤ Tideslow Rake

In 1577 when Francis Drake set sail on his venture to discover the New World a certain John Dolphin was contemplating the potential of venturing underground in the area of what became High Rake Mine. By the 1700s numerous other miners and prospectors searching for their own adventure and spoils were beginning to reap the rewards from their mines along the rake. Little Hucklow Liberty encompassed the hamlets of Coplow Dale, Little Hucklow and Windmill and stretched west from 'Bradda' (Bradwell) Lane to the old Castleton Road.

Evidence of lead mining activity on the High Rake can still be seen in the disturbed ground running parallel with and immediately behind the line of houses at Windmill. The rake then crosses Washers Lane in front of the agricultural shed following the Parish boundary. On the south side a line of depressions follows the wall line. Here beyond the turning for Poynton Cross Farm is the 700 feet deep High Rake mine-shaft, now capped and part of the archaeological site excavated by PDHMS. Looking west across the old Castleton

Road at the hillside (now an SSI site) you can see the Tideslow Rake tumbling down the hillside

Beyond the agricultural shed running parallel to the main rake on the north side, there are three lines of hillocks in the fields. The line of the field wall marks the Washers Vein as it streaks westward crossing Washers Lane before opening out in a field of broken ground close by the Old Castleton Road.

To the north-west, along Forest Lane, we have more disturbed land known as Maiden Rake. This joins Brockholes or Brockwall vein that stretches east towards the Bradwell Road just south of the main street in Little Hucklow.

The shafts and mines along and beside the main High Rake vein, together with the landscape, tell many stories. Some mines were named after their owners, such as Valentine, and others after their position, such as Nether Liberty and Cow Pasture. Folk-lore may hold the origins of some but the very names such as Mock, Ready Money, Foxes Venture and Luck in a Bag conjure up the hopes and fears of their miners.

View to the east along Tideslow Rake towards Windmill

The surviving part of a typical miner's cottage in Windmill.

The village of Little Hucklow

There are three significant developments which illustrate the importance of Little Hucklow Liberty at this time:

- The miners of this liberty helped by men from Tideswell organised themselves into a group to challenge the Lords of the Manor at Little Hucklow over the rights to free mining in the late 1500s and early 1600s.
- Small and Great Barmote Courts sat at Windmill. Kenneth Cameron, in his '*Place Names of Derbyshire*', quotes a 1607 reference to the hamlet as 'The Windmilne House' and we know from early mining documents that the Barmote Court sat at the Windmill House. (Barmote Court, see chapter on Customs and Laws, p20).
- In 1758 there was a plan to build the Sheffield to Buxton turnpike through Windmill to transport the lead and its workers which indicates its importance at that time. This was before Tideswell, with its commercial businesses and market charter, demanded that the turnpike should be re-routed. The hamlet was marked on the 1791 Burdett's map as Windmill Houses.

We know from a plan at Chatsworth in the Devonshire collection that there were some named mine shafts along the main vein stretching from the end of Windmill to the old Castleton Road.

This document was not dated but we can trace, through the ore accounts and bills of complaint from the Barmote Court records, that these mines existed at least in the 17th Century.

There is also a list of mines and mine owners in the Bagshawe Collection, which again is unfortunately undated, but it was probably written before 1769 since one of the major shareowners mentioned, Aymer Rich, had died in that year. JH Rieuwerts uses this list to conclude that earlier shafts and grooves along the rake were incorporated into three main mines: Mock, Luck in the Bag (High Rake) and Valentine. He realised that the number of meers belonging to the three main mines along the rake were equal to the sum of the meers of the smaller mines recorded in the list of mines (SA-BC 671/6).

Two minor veins ran alongside the main High Rake vein, close to the agricultural shed in Washers Lane above Windmill. On the south side of the road, below the plantation, was Birchen Lee mine that, with Mock and Valentine mines, was considered for re-opening in the 1930s. On the north side was Cow Pasture mine. Over to the west of Little Hucklow village is Maiden Rake Vein which was the scene of conflict between the miners of little Hucklow Liberty and Tideswell Liberty in 1765.

The Liberty in the 1800s saw a number of mines

Aerial view of Windmill showing working on the rake behind the cottages

being bought and sold. Around 1834 William Wyatt of Foolow, mine agent and shareholder in the mines bought up further shares in several mines for himself and others. Two more mines were founded, Ready Money and Foxes Venture.

'Benjamin Wyatt then gave on behalf of Mr Thomas Birds and the rest of his partners at a mine called Fox Venture one dish of ore to Mr Francis Heyward, Barmaster for the said Liberty to free a Founder Meer in an old vein on the north side Valentine Title, Liberty of Hucklow, November 12th 1817' (John Goodchild Collection).

Lead mining had declined by the 1900s but mining and hillocking for fluorspar increased, providing some return for mine owners.

Conflict

Free mining was beset with difficulties in the sixteenth century: lords of the manor often conflicted with the crown in trying to establish their control of the mining rights on their lands.

In 1597, Ursula Slater and Ralph Blackwall claimed the lot and cope in the manor of Little Hucklow. This prompted John Burton of Tideswell, described as a poor miner, to make a stand for his rights of free mining at Little Hucklow by using the Barmote Court. Unfortunately he lost the case, but a precedent was set.

In 1612 there was further opposition to landowners. Ralphe Oldfield of Litton led a group of Tideswell and Litton miners to dig in Little Hucklow Manor and was opposed by the Lady of the Manor, Isabel Bowes, who was the former wife of Sir William Foljambe of Walton near Chesterfield. This family had maintained control over the production of lead since the 1570's and was not going to relinquish their rights so easily. It took another three years through the courts and another petition by 50 miners before the Eyre family, as lessee of the lot and cope for the Crown, guaranteed the right of free mining in the manor.

Barmote Court

The Barmote Court records are a valuable resource for investigating our mining heritage. The hamlet of Windmill, between Great and Little Hucklow villages and flanking the boundary of the two liberties, held the Barmote Court on several occasions at Windmill House, a bulding which no longer exsts. The court was here as early as 1669 and again in 1743, 1749, 1752 and 1761.

'The Great Barmoot court of our Soverign Lord the King held by the Most Noble Wm. Duke of Devonshire at Windmill house in the liberty of Great Hucklow within and for the said jurisdiction the 12th of October 1749 before Thomas Barker Gentleman Steward there' (Chatsworth Devonshire Collection)

The jury of 24 included many whose names appear in papers and manuscripts about lead mining. Higginbottom, Oldfield, Redfearn, Howe, Bramwell, Needham, Low and Valentine Furnice have all been mentioned. When a miner had appeared before the court he was not precluded or disqualified from serving on the jury. Mr Furnice was a juror in 1749 but in 1752 Mr R White complained against him for not paying £2 7s 1d (£300 in 2008 using the retail price index).

Court expenses covered the steward's fee, dinner at the steward's table with ale for the jurors. Music, pipes and tobacco were also enjoyed. The jurisdiction of the Barmote Court and its appointed officials was respected and upheld across the mining fraternity and the official records have proved an invaluable source of evidence.

Early mines

The structure of the rake in this area gave rise to many small mines which were eventually consolidated with other mines to form a larger concern. The vein was a fissure or fault in the rock strata formed from the movement of the earth and subsequently filled with various minerals including galena (lead ore). Often there were several parallel fractures of varying length so that in the early days many small mines could be driven at intervals along the same vein which as the levels coincided might be consolidated into one mine.

More evidence about the earlier mines shown on the plan in the Devonshire Collection is revealed in the dated ore accounts of Jacob Holmes of Winster (Devonshire Collection) that show, for example, production at three of the mines:

6 months ending Michelmas (Sept) 1734
    Willson Old Groove - 28 dishes
    Dudings Groove - 23 dishes
6 months ending Ladyday(April) 1735
    Willson Old Groove -54 dishes
    Duding - Tall Hill -28 dishes

Michelmas 1735 - 1736
  Willsons Old Groove - 83 dishes
  Dudings & Mortin - 27 dishes
  Tall Hills - 32 dishes

This record also shows that Duding's Groove changed to Dudding-Tall Hill, which is associated with High Rake mine. Tall Hills becomes a separate mine in 1736. According to JH Rieuwerts, the 19th Century High Rake mine shaft was between Dudin's 2nd shaft and Houson's shaft. In June 1749 Tall Hill, including High Rake, merged with Luck in the Bag or Little Groove Engine.

Bills of Complaint

An insight into the trials and tribulations of those early miners who worked on the rake can also be traced through the Barmote Court records, in the Barmasters' Calendar 'Bills of Complaints'. The cases illustrate how important it was to have a miners' court to settle often complicated disputes and act as a deterrent to devious behaviour.

The case of Thomas Duddin is an example. At the great Barmote Court held at Smalldale on the 10th April 1739, John Soresbey complained against Thomas Duddin and his partners for concealing four dishes of ore at 'Dudins' Grove. Thomas Duddin claimed he could prove the ore had been measured in front of John Soresbey. But the court found in favour of John Soresbey. Thomas had to forfeit the four ore dishes. The ore buyer, Issac Morten, was also fined ten shillings. These were heavy penalties and costly mistakes.

Issac Morten was also fined 20 shillings in a complaint by John Soresby for unlawful measuring and concealment of ore from the Maiden Rake grove. For this, the partners John Nodder, Thomas Middleton and Richard Hill, forfeited 40 dishes – about four and a half loads. Ore accounts of four years earlier recorded that 80 dishes had been mined during the six months Michelmas 1735 to Lady Day 1736. If we assume their production was similar at the later date, roughly three months' work was lost by their actions.

We might presume from this account that both the miner and the ore buyer were trying to get out of paying lot and cope; not an oversight on their part but a deliberate attempt at evading duty. They thought it was an acceptable risk, but to their own detriment. They also lost their reputations. Many miners worked long hard hours for little return. The courts were in no doubt that they had to have heavy punishments to stem the practice.

A second example showes that Adam Wilson & Partners of Wilson Old Grove on Hucklow Old Rake were having difficulties in October 1745 and again in April 1746. The following people filed claims for debts: Thomas Duddon 19/8d, Samuel Bunting 7/4d and Edward Barber 14/- All claims were upheld by the jury of 24 men.

Samuel Bunting of Windmill was a blacksmith, much in demand for tools such as drills and picks that always needed sharpening. Samuel complained at Bradwell on 22 October, 1745 against Thomas Duddin of Smalldale and partners about their interests at Luck in the Bag mine on Hucklow Old Rake, which they were either working or had shares. The case was upheld in favour of Samuel and he was paid £1 6s 9d. At the same court he made a complaint William Low & Partners at Nether Close mine, but for only 4s 8d. He won.

Samuel Bunting hadn't done so well at an earlier court. In 1739 when he complained against the partners of Tall Hill mine, for 18s 8d for blacksmith work he was awarded only 8s 8d because the case was contested by partners Isaac Hill and Edward Morton.

Many problems arose because miners couldn't trust various partners, traders and service providers or couldn't count on them in times of need.

The miners generally respected and upheld the jurisdiction of the Barmote Court and its appointed officials, the Barmasters. That they stayed within the laws and customs without too much trouble is an achievement to be admired.

Luck in the Bag

High Rake Mine (discussed by John Barnatt in the following section)was previously known in the 1760s as Luck in the Bag, with about 18 meers having incorporated several smaller shafts and mines as noted on the plan in the Devonshire Collection. Rieuwerts explains that if we combine Houson's shaft of 131 yards and the two Dudins's titles of 95 and 127 yards, add 222 yards of High Rake we have a total of 575 yards which is close to 18 meers (32yards x 18) that equals Luck in a Bag Mine.

There were 14 shareholders most with small interests of 1/24th, 1/48th or 1/96th. The two major shareholders were Mr Green and Mr Longdon each with 1/6 The mine was valued at £480 in 1767.

Work started in 1768 to sink deeper, and by 1783 the miners had reached a depth of 61 fathoms (366 feet). Another seven fathoms (42 feet) were added in 1784 and ore production in 1785 was recorded as 157 loads (39 tons) with another 121 loads (30 tons) produced the following year.

Although water was not a major problem some accumulated waters were drained westwards through a drift that emptied into the Tideslow swallow.

A small notebook in the Sheffield Archives entitled 'High Rake' records:

> 'Let this day to Henry Marchington the Old Ground at High Rake mine until Christmas 1806 being east of the engine shaft on the following conditions only. To pay to the proprietors 6s per load on all the ore he gets and 4s per load on all the belland he gets, to give the overseer Notice of measuring 2 days before any is measured to continue works the said place with no less than 6 pairs of hands otherwise the proprietors to be at liberty to let it to any other persons. Henry McIntosh to smelt all the ore and belland he gets up and the High Rake partners to have the lead arising from such ore and belland paying him for it at same price as they give for lead at the Dale cupolas.'

High Rake Mining Company was formed in 1834 by William Wyatt of Foolow, but the mine itself was often referred to as Luck in the Bag.

Valentine mine

Jacob Holmes of Winster left another notebook which is now in the Derby Record Office. Between December 25th and March 25th 1727 ore extracted at Valentine Furness Grove amounted to two loads five dishes, around half a ton. Valentine Furness's shaft was 233 yards west of the Bradwell Road.

We also know from the Bills of Complaint that, in 1746, a Valentine Furness worked for a mine called Nalls Grove in Little Hucklow liberty as he claimed for non-payment of his wages (17s 11d) from George Eyre.

Valentine mine was later called Consolidated with 16 meers. This implies that some earlier shafts and grooves along the rake were incorporated into this title. We are not sure which these were but, if we refer again the plan in the Devonshire Collection and take into account the meers designated to each, Rieuwerts suggests that Valentine Furness and Adam Wilson Groove formed part of that title. Shareholders named were:

Joshua Needham 1/4 share, Aymer Rich Esq, Wm. & Jn. Bagshaw Esq, Mr Jasper & Samuel Frith, Mr Richard White, John Wilkinson (1/12th) Mr Hall, George Barnsley, Samuel Bunting, John Bramwell (1/24th)

The next we hear of Valentine mine is from the Mary Rodes accounts of 1770 when her 1/12th share had incurred costs of £2.11s2d. Mary was the niece of Aymer Rich. Her accounts show:

- Outgoings included payments for wages, ropes, boards and horses. William Low was employed to clear gates, draw clay and timbering as well as to drive a tunnel five fathoms west, some of it being paid at 25s a fathom.
- William Blackwell was meanwhile busy sinking a shaft and sump to the engine shaft foot, which cost about £7. Ralph Blackwell was paid 28/6d per load of ore, which amounted to £3.16s for two loads six dishes. William Low was paid only 27 shillings a load for five loads three dishes, a total of £7.4s.

Miners often negotiated, with their mine

A cluster of mountain pansies often found growing on the the old lead mine sites in the Little Hucklow Liberty

owners, their own contracts called bargains. These were for short periods, to extract ore based on their initial assumption of how much was there, how to extract it and the market at the time. The owners had to decide how much to pay while judging a futures market so they would sell to make an early profit. A mistake could be costly.

In 1773 Mary had a profit of 1s 10d. In January, Ralph Blackwell and John Bramwell charged ore at the same price of 28s 6d. By April of that year, the charges had gone down to 27 shillings per load. Re-negotiation followed as this was not profitable.

Joshua Needham's wage had gone down from £1 6s to just 13s and stayed at that even in 1778 when next we know of her accounts. The 2008 values of these amounts are £128 and £64 respectively.

Later, in 1787, Mary Rodes took Joshua, now the Barmaster, to court for neglecting his duties to her in respect of her mining interests. This is discussed further in the Great Hucklow Liberty section (p 61).

By June 28th 1778, the total costs had fallen to £20 8s 10d, offset further by a deduction of ore sales at £6.3s.6d. Mary's 1/12th share of profit was 2s 11d. Was this venture worth such a small return? Although profits were small, people were being employed; materials were being bought and used or perhaps they were stored as an asset that might realise some gain in the share value.

More than thirty years passed before Valentine was mentioned again. From some notes 'Profits at Valentine of sundry persons' we know that in November 1812 a Mr Nall appeared to be mining on his own at Valentine mine, producing nine loads at a profit of 13s 8d.

During 1813 he was joined by a Samuel Bunting and for that year made £6 16s (£325 at today's prices) and mined over 25 tons of ore.

In 1814, George Fox joined the team and they continued to mine together profitably for about ten years until 1825 when Mr Nall left.

More partners joined over the next few years: Bagshaw, Ashton and Cheetam. George Fox stayed until 1831.

For the year 1828, a total of 194 loads 5 dishes of belland was extracted.

'Belland was the very fine particles of lead ore produced during the dressing process. It became a viable by-product after the introduction of the

cupola smelting furnace in the 1730s. The old waste heaps were constantly raked over to reclaim every last dot.'

In 1834 Samuel Bunting of Windmill and William Bramwell of Eyam sold their 1/24th shares in Valentine mine near Windmill to William Wyatt for £1 each .

Mock Mine

Mock Mine had five meers at the western end of the liberty near the old Castleton road. One was Robert Cleaton's meer of 1654 which allowed the mine to drain through the Tideslow Old/Poyton Cross swallow. It was owned in the 1700s by Joshua Swindle, Westby Hadfield, Richard, William and John Bagshaw.

The mine stopped working in 1826 and in 1827 a loss was recorded. In 1828, Josiah Ash collected belland of seven loads four dishes in June and, in December, Hannah Walker collected 11 loads. Thomas Blackwell, for Matthew Frost the Barmaster, recorded a total of 37 loads 5 dishes in the Hucklow ore accounts of 1829.

The mine had seven meers by 1829. The Barmote Court registered an interest in 1831, suggesting some discontent in the management of the mine. On the 4th April 1835 a loss of £131 0s 10d was recorded. Sixteen men were employed for

'stempling and repairing way gates and engine shaft, making a housing over the shaft foot and driving a wagon road eastwardly from the engine shaft at 47 fathoms deep, laying down oak and iron rails and finishing the same in a good workmanlike manner'.

The wages bill alone, apart from the cost of materials and services, came to £60 9s 0d paid at two shillings a day.

In 1835 there appeared to be debts between various parties but by May 12th 1835 the case was abandoned and the shares of the mine sold on the 13th July to William Wyatt acting on behalf of the High Rake Company. Seventeen shareholders of Mock Mine sold their interest for £100 16s 7d (£8,354 in 2008) to Mr Wyatt, a major shareholder. He now held 17/24ths of this mine along with some partners:

George Dicken 2/24th
Samuel Bennett 2/24th
Amorias Sutton 1/24th

Joseph Swindell 1/24th

The Reverend George Brown 1/24th

total 24/24th

In 1880 Martha Redfearn, landlady of the Red Lion Inn at Windmill, owned Mock Mine. She was extracting ore from a level, which had been driven under the Castleton road to a mine in the neighbouring Tideslow liberty. Mr Wake, a solicitor of Sheffield who owned the Hucklow Hall estate, was contesting her right to bring up ore through the shaft on his land when it had been gained outside the boundary of the Little Hucklow liberty and brought a case of trespass.

Martha in her turn maintained she could not afford to sink another shaft, which would cost between £700 and £800. The Lord Chief justice's final ruling after an appeal had been brought was a 'body blow' for small mining concerns as he found in favour of the plaintiff, Mr Wake. Mrs Redfearn explained that if a miner had to sink a shaft to bring out ore in the land of every surface owner whose land he worked, mining would be prohibitively expensive.

The mining laws, revised in the High Peak Mining Customs and Mineral Act of 1851, on which the judgement was based, were now in favour of the landowner. Wake was also alleging that Mrs Redfearn had brought up a quantity of spar which was very valuable and which she had failed to hand over to him. Presumably by this time most of the lead ore had been extracted and what was now being mined was spar with small amounts of lead in it.

According to the 1851 Act, spar was the property of the surface owner and lead ore of the mine owner. Fluorspar by this time was increasingly becoming the valuable asset, so the act again favoured the landowner. The headlines for the reports of the case in several newspapers of July 10th 1880 show how important it was considered for setting a precedent. In spite of or indeed because of the revised laws of 1851 disputes still arose between landowners and miners.

Buying & Selling

Throughout the early 1800s a number of mines and shares in mines changed hands. Apart from the four mines below the rest of the mines are dealt with under their separate mine headings.

1. Robert Cooper of Sheffield sold to Thomas Wragg of Little Hucklow 'one half of a mine' they had between them in Little Hucklow for £78 16s. A substantial sum in 1829, equivalent to £5,600 in 2008. The name of the mine is not mentioned.
2. The Dickens family of Windmill, William, Richard and Joseph sold to Martin Chapman of Little Hucklow 12/24ths of a mine called Green Rake for £6 in 1834.
3. On the 27th February 1841 Brockwall mine south east of the village of Little Hucklow, was sold by William Oldfield of Tideswell Moor to John Bagshaw for £4. There were ten meers.
4. George Fox sold his share of 8/24 of Fox Venture close to Windmill for £1.

Ready Money

On the 24th February, 1841 John Bramwell agreed to buy from George Barker of Foolow all of his title to Ready Money mine behind Windmill for £1 10s. Two days later, on the 26th February, 1841 John Bramwell extended his ownership by buying, for £4, all titles in the mine from John Bagshaw of Grindlow plus eight meers at the east end of the land from Isaac Watts of Chapel-en-le-Frith.

In January 1842 John Bramwell sold Ready Money to Isaac Watts for just one shilling. Isaac already owned the field in Windmill that was used by John's father Francis.

Why did he sell? He gained no lead ore, so far as we know, and he lost about £5. Did he find nothing and was glad of a shilling or didn't he have the means to continue mining?

Lime Kiln Mine

Sometime between June 1841 and June 1842, John Bramwell of Windmill and Joshua Walker and John Needham of Gt. Hucklow sold their shares in Lime Kiln vein, on the north side of Valentine and High Rake mines, to William Wyatt. John Barnatt suggests that William might have bought this vein so that water could be pumped from High Rake shaft to pass over Lime Kiln vein to be discharged further down the valley well away from High Rake so that it would not re-enter the workings. This coincided with a Cornish steam engine being installed at the mine for pumping.

Birchen-Lee Mine / Who Can Tell mine

According to the Hucklow ore account of December 8th 1827, William Oldfield was producing about six dishes each of ore and belland from Who Can Tell mine. The following year, on the 12th May 1828, William Dicken worked one load of ore and six dishes of belland at Birchen Lee also known as Who Can Tell mine.

Samuel Bunting bought Birchen-Lee mine from William and Hugh Oldfield of Windmill in December 1839 for £4. A few days later, he offered a 12½% share plus ore found to sink a shaft. On completion Samuel would either work the mine or pay a quarter share of the sinking.

Cow Pasture Vein

The bills of complaint registered with the Barmote Court show that on the 21st April 1730, Edward Ashton was working Cow Pasture mine and had failed to receive his wages of 11 shillings from William Drabble & Partners. A few years later, in 1739, there was a further failure by James Sidwall of Hope & Partners to pay £2 4s 10d to Samuel Bunting, the blacksmith.

In 1738 Robert French pursued a claim in 1738 through the Barmote Court at Windmill against William Low of Bradwell for 'unjustly entering into and detaining from the complainant one half of a grove in the Cow Pasture, formerly known as 'New mine' '. French said that Low carried away 20 loads, about five tons, of lead ore.

In April 1740, Edward May was owed about £34 by William Cowley & Partners at 'Hucklow North Vein mine' at the 'Cow Pasture Field Side'. He also lodged a complaint at the same time against John & Benjamin Hallam of Stony Middleton for not paying £4 9s 8d at 'Fieldside Groove'.

At the same time Hellen Roger wanted payment of 15s 3d for her work at 'Field Side mine' from Mr May and Mr Spenser. This was probably hillocking, the reworking of old spoil heaps, usually done by women. Joseph Masden of Stony Middleton also wanted £3 16s 6d for work at the mine. It cost them 1s 4d each to present the bill of complaint but the court found in their favour.

Mr Spencer also appeared to have interests in the 'Cow Pasture Mine' as, with other partners, he was cited as owing wages to Samuel Bingham of £3 11s 4d.

In 1766 at Cow Pasture mine, the partners Robert & William Bagshaw, Aymer Rich and Jos Needham agreed to sink a drift or level through their swallow hole to dewater the mines at Smithy Coe in Hucklow at their cost.

There is no evidence that this work was done, but it might have started. According to Mrs Mary Rodes accounts from Ladyday (March) to Michaelmas (September) 1770 there was work at Cow Pasture Swallow with costs for six months at £21 16s 8d. This included-

- George Hill, driving north seven fathoms at 30 shillings a fathom, was paid £10 10s.
- William Low drew clay and timber and was paid £2 as well as a further £2 for driving a wagon and £1 for getting stone and walling.
- Joshua Needham provided boards of five score at £2 1s 8d possibly for shoring up tunnels, as flooring for corves (trucks, tubs or baskets used in a mine) or for a cart gate.
- Thomas Frogget-Smith: a bill of £1 18s 6d for

Cow Pasture Hillocks

the use of horses

- An item called an 'earnest' was also included. For this period it was four shillings. (This was a day's wage given to miners as an incentive at the beginning of their bargain or before completion).

Throughout 1773 Mary incurred costs. Records for the years to June 1778 are not available but then after paying costs she had a small profit of 1s 8d as her sixth share from some twelve dishes of ore. In October 1778 she had a profit of 1s 9d before again having to find costs of 17s in April 1779. It looks as if this project to unwater the mines was also a drain on financial resources and consequently failed.

At Nether liberty mine (referred to under Great Hucklow Liberty p 58) on the eastern edge of Windmill, the miners already drained water from the Hucklow Edge mines into a swallow hole but this was unable to cope with the volume. They might have alleviated this by connecting to Swallow Grove mine to lower their water table.

Maiden Rake

At Maiden Rake on September 18th 1765 there was a dispute between Jonathan Oxley of Leam (Eyam parish) & Partners and Mrs Eleanor Green and Partners over title to a primgap. A primgap was part of a meer in a vein that was less than half a meer long, and was where the vein ranged into another liberty. Joshua Needham Barmaster for Little Hucklow had in May of that year stopped a primgap of nine yards in Maiden Rake vein.

The vein stretched over two liberties: it was called Maiden Rake in Little Hucklow Liberty which was in the Kingsfield and Chapmaiden in Tideswell Liberty where the duties of Lot and Cope were claimed by the Lord of the Manor and 'farmed out'. The plaintiff, Eleanor Green, wanted to claim possession of the primgap. The defendant, Jonathan Oxley, had bought the whole title of Maiden Rake in 1750 without knowing anything of the primgap. In 1764 he had freed and staked out a founder meer taking in the old primgap and had sunk a shaft through the channel (toadstone) to a lower level to find a productive vein.

Mrs Green had also found a productive vein at the same level from her side and wanted to bring it eastwards through the Kingsfield before Oxley reached it and could prevent her claim.

The case notes referred back to Richard Hill, a working miner and shareholder who, in 1747, bought the primgap for his own convenience. He had interests in both mines at the same time, but failed to place a shaft on the Maiden Rake Vein in the Kingsfield (Little Hucklow Liberty) to mark his rights. The ore mined on this side was removed through the primgap via Chapmaiden in Tideswell Liberty. Oxley considered that the duty ore was fraudulently and clandestinely taken by Mr Morten, the farmer of the Tideswell duties and a partner at both mines and father of Eleanor Green (see Bills of Complaint for further reference to Isaac Morten and Richard Hill).

Nicking the mines

At the end of August 1908 the Barmaster, George Eagle used the customary mining laws to full

Maiden Rake from Forest Lane

advantage when he formally nicked the Mock and Fox's Venture mines near Windmill by displaying notices giving the owners three weeks in which to work the mines. The mines were not worked and were subsequently handed over to Mr Harrison of Tideswell, who represented a company opening up works nearby.

'The ancient custom of handing over a piece of spar to denote the new owner was dispensed with, as it had no legal standing. Not until the name of the new owner was entered into the Barmaster's book was evidence of the ownership noted.' (19/9/1908, High Peak News).

The old method of 'nicking' a mine by nicking the stow was dispensed with after the Act of 1851, although the custom continued (see Customs and Laws, p21).

The following year, around March, Buxton solicitors Shipton & Ainsworth represented Leon Harrison, grocer of Tideswell. They registered the transfer of the Mock and Fox's Venture and other nearby mines, including Ready Money and Valentine to Matthew Dickie of Ravens Tor, Millers Dale, and William Christopher Mallison of Cressbrook Hall, both manufacturers. These two continued to work the mines and other works as the Litton Mineral Company. Mr Harrison continued in his own name as a producer of stone.

This custom was used again in 1937, in trying to reactivate Mock, High Rake, Valentine, Ready Money, Foxes Venture, Birchen Lee and some of the mines in Great Hucklow liberty. A notice in the Queen Anne public house signed by the Barmaster of the High Peak, John Mort a Manchester mining surveyor, announced:

'Notice is hereby given, that these mines situate in the liberty of the Kingsfield in the Hundred of the High Peak in the County of Derby will be forfeited at the expiration of three weeks from the date hereof if not duly and reasonably worked to the satisfaction of the Barmaster and the Grand Jury and if no sufficient reason be assigned to them' (Manchester Guardian August 18th 1937)

At this time the price of lead was forced up to £24 a ton, due to re-armament work, and fluorspar also had become a valuable commodity. It might well have been seen by those entrepreneurs that acquiring the lease and working these outlying deposits could be worthwhile.

These are only a few of the stories associated with Little Hucklow Liberty. Undoubtedly there are many more to be found.

Windmill House in Hucklow - court Charges March 23rd 1761	
Stewards Fee	£1 .. 1 .. 0
Dined at stewards table 34	£1 .. 14 .. 0
Ale to ditto	£2 .. 0 .. 0
Dined at 24 mens table 31	15 .. 6
Ale to ditto	£2 .. 11 .. 0
Music	2 .. 0
Hay & corn	3 .. 6
Pipes & tobacco	2 .. 0
Barrkeeper	5 .. 0
Ale given to miners	£1 .. 16 .. 0
	£10 .. 10 .. 0
Received the aforesaid sum in full by me George Dicken	

Barmote Court expenses. (Chatsworth Devonshire MSS)

5. High Rake Mine

Some ventures struck very lucky on the Hucklow Vein, others did not; High Rake Mine, in the Liberty of Little Hucklow, was one of the latter. A great deal of time, money and effort was invested by the shareholders and their mine agent during the latter part of its development in the hopes of a good return. It was certainly a 'high tech' mine of its day, but sunk in exactly the wrong place, as described in the following section.

A view of part of the excavated mine site today.

This section describing High Rake Mine has been written for us by Dr John Barnatt, Senior Survey Archaeologist with the Peak District National Park Authority, and also Conservation Officer for the Peak District Mines Historical Society. His piece is based on an eight-year archaeological survey, exploration and restoration of the site by a project team from PDMHS which has revealed the original functions of the structures from what little now remains of this once extensive lead mining site.

We are very grateful to John and his team for allowing us the benefit of their work and expertise.

John Barnatt showing the base of one of the High Rake Mine chimneys to a group of visitors to the site.

employees. Similarly, from 1834 to when the mine closed, much of the blacksmithing was done by William Barnes of Eyam and the carpenters work was undertaken by Nathaniel Somersett from near Wardlow Mires.

Many tradesmen were involved in erecting the mine buildings. In 1842 William Morton, a mason from Froggatt, won the contract to create the pumping house and later also lined the shaft. A relative, Jonathan Morton, had the quarry on Bretton Moor used for the gritstone ashlar. Other craftsmen included: Nathaniel Somersett – carpentry: John Brocklehurst – plastering: R. Hill - glazing and painting: and W. Hall – roof slating. Many others are named as supplying and carting materials. The 1847 winding house was built by William Chapman and Co and other specialist craftsmen and suppliers are again named. Once the engines were up and running large amounts of coal were needed and much of this was supplied by William Booker and Co, who owned Green Lane Colliery at Dronfield.

The Mine Site Today

At the centre of the site is the engine shaft (Fig. 5:A). This is oval and was once divided vertically by boards into pumping, winding and climbing compartments. It is 720 feet (219m) deep! The uppermost part, through raised and unstable ground, is lined with stone walling known as ginging. Starting at 255-275 feet (78-84m) down, after a long section sunk in solid limestone, fine-quality ashlar lining retains the rotted-toadstone sides. This ashlar was seen in 2003 when a one-off descent by winch was undertaken to record the shaft. On the day of exploration, in low summer conditions, the water that had flooded much of the mine was encountered at 322 feet (98m) down. Here a miner's wooden ladder protrudes from 398 feet (121m) of water.

There is now nothing to be seen of the large wooden headframe over the shaft, which supported pulleys for ropes used for winding stone and ore out of the shaft, and for letting down large cast iron 'pump pipes', 'pump rods' and other heavy mine equipment.

Today the most impressive surface feature is the 1842-3 'house' (Fig. 5:B, 6) for the pumping engine installed to keep the mine free of water (Fig. 11). Excavations have shown that the bottom third of this building remains, set below ground level (Figs 12,13). The main internal space, which is 16 feet (5m) deep, contained the lower 70-inch diameter cylinder of the engine, fitted snugly in the half furthest away from the shaft. The base of this cylinder was set on a platform, probably supported by horizontal iron beams, about 5.9 feet (1.8m) above the rock-cut floor. When the engine was being installed or afterwards, the engineer must have become concerned for its stability, for two stout timber posts were placed vertically to support the platform from beneath. The postholes cut into the rock can still be seen. The high-pressure upper cylinder, of 36-inch diameter, with a shared piston rod with that below, was within the next room up, which had a floor roughly coincident with the surrounding ground level and the top of the lower cylinder. The piston rod rose and was connected to one end of a massive, 33 feet 4 inch (10m) long cast-iron beam placed horizontally high above, the ends of which rocked up and down. This pivoted on the bob-wall, built thicker to take the weight, at about 30 feet (9m) above the present wall top. The other end of the beam protruded over the shaft to where it was connected to a substantial vertically-placed timber, 11 inches (28cm) across, known as a pump rod. A set of these went down the shaft for nearly its full depth with one timber strapped to the next. The engine, via the rocking beam, made the 'pump rods' move up and down, which in turn operated pumps within the shaft. These forced water up large-diameter cast-iron pipes in the shaft to surface, where it was mostly channelled away from the mine to the valley to the north. A small amount would be used to top up the steam engine reservoir and the condenser tank.

Between the engine house and the shaft there is an impressive condenser pit (Fig. 5:C, 12), which is 8m deep from the shaft collar to its floor. This pit contained a large tank of water, within which sat the condenser into which steam from the engine was passed. The cold water condensed the steam to form a vacuum in the engine cylinder, giving it considerably greater power than the original Newcomen-type 18th Century steam engines. The tank was supported on timber beams set on side plinths, with a central space between, where there was a small wooden drain that took any

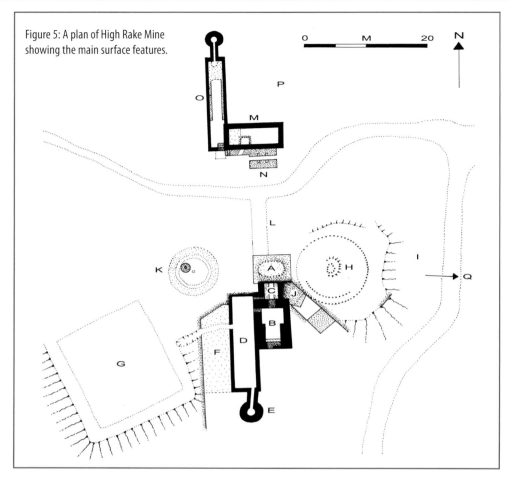

Figure 5: A plan of High Rake Mine showing the main surface features.

water leakage into the engine- and boiler-houses back to the main shaft.

To the side of the engine house is its boiler house (Figs. 5, 6), again sunk into the ground. This was not emptied to its full depth during the recent excavations because the original side-walls had developed inward leans and were unstable (the upper parts you see today have largely been rebuilt). The building contained a main boiler of cylindrical Cornish type, which was 34 feet (10.5m) long and filled much of the building except for a stoking area at the north end. Behind is the flue to the base of a large chimney which was once 59 feet (18m) high (Fig. 5:E). A small boiler, only 6 feet (1.8m) long, was used to help start the engine. To one side is the cobbled yard for the prodigious amounts of coal needed to power this engine (Fig. 5:F, 6, 11); coal dust can still be seen between the stones. Beyond is the retained bank of the now-backfilled reservoir for

both steam engines (Fig. 5:G). The gap in the coal yard cobbling is where the pipework to the boiler house was removed in 1853.

The 'pump rods' and 'pump pipes' in the shaft were enormously heavy. They were lowered into place by a large hand-operated capstan, located on a raised platform immediately east of the shaft (Fig. 5:H). The platform needed to be large to accommodate the many men at the long arms of the capstan when it was being used in earnest. In 1853 a large gin engine was erected here to wind ore from underground during reworking of the unflooded upper parts of the mine, after the steam engines and other fixtures, including the capstan, had been sold off. A low central mound contains a hollow at the site of the bearing block for the central vertical axial-post. When first excavated, slight wear grooves in the gravel floor could clearly be seen where the horses walked in a circle as they pulled the winding drum round. Nothing remains of smithy and carpenter's shop, which the old site photograph shows was of two storeys and lay between the platform and the farm track.

Next to the condenser pit there is a raised stone platform for a second large cast-iron rocking beam known as a 'balance bob' (Fig. 5:J). This beam has one end going diagonally into the shaft where it was connected to the 'pump rods'. The other end had a large box filled with scrap iron, which dropped into the adjacent shallow pit and acted as a counterweight when the steam engine raised the 'pump rods'. These rods were extremely heavy and lifting them was the engine's primary task, the counterweight made a significant difference to its efficiency and thus running costs.

On the opposite side of the shaft are the remains of a horse-drawn ore-crusher (Fig. 5:K), again used after 1853 (Fig. 7). A horse pulled the crushing stone round in a circle and ore was shovelled beneath it. The site is dished in shape and must have collected water, so a re-used cast-iron pipe was inserted to drain it to lower ground nearby. The production of mineral gravel, in this case crushed between the iron tyre and an iron crushing bed, was the first stage of the 'dressing' process in which the ore was concentrated by removal of the other material with which it is mixed. After crushing, as the lead ore was far denser than the other crushed minerals and rock, when the gravel was suspended in water, the ore could easily be separated because it settled out first. The first dressing floors may have been somewhere near the horse-drawn crusher and ore dressing presumably again took place here from 1853, but between 1847 and 1852 the dressing was semi-mechanized and took place close to the steam engine to the north.

Figure 6: The pumping engine house complex in 2007 during the last phase of consolidation. The condenser pit under the scaffolding platform is 8m deep. Behind, from left to right, are the engine house, the part-excavated boiler house with chimney base at the back, and the coal yard.

Figure 7: Part of the horse-drawn ore crusher after excavation. The iron tyre on the fallen crushing stone, together with its iron crushing bed, had been removed long before. Note the notches on the stone for the wedges used to tighten the tyre. When first dug, lines of rust could be seen following the two edges of the circular crushing bed. Most of the outer shovelling floor had also been robbed, except where it lay under a small 20th Century spoil heap next to a trial reworking pit.

Figure 8: At the back of the winding house this large beam was carefully set on a buried plinth and had been precisely levelled using timbers and chock stones; it may well have supported machinery (of unknown character). As with the last example, such details are only found with careful excavation.

Set back from the shaft to the north, beyond the presumed site of the 1834-1847 gin engine of which there is now no trace (Fig. 5:L), are the foundations of the largely-removed 1847 'house' (Fig. 5:M) for the steam winding engine bought from Magpie Mine (Barnatt and Vernon 2007). The four walls are all of the same thickness indicating the engine's beam was placed completely within the building rather than resting on a thick bob wall with half protruding beyond. Outside the engine house to the south side a raised inspection walkway, built in stone, led to machinery set above plinths, the bases of the slots for its four fastening bolts still remain (Fig. 5:N). These held down either the gearing mechanism for a winding drum, or the documented rolls crushers installed for ore processing, both of which are likely to have been somewhere in this vicinity. Outside the other side of the building there is curious timber beam once set into the wall (Fig. 8).

To the west of the winding house are the foundations of its boiler house (Fig. 5:O), with flue and small chimney beyond. At the south end steps lead down into the stoking area, with coal fragments still visible on the gravel floor. Beyond was a single Cornish boiler, with a small paved area behind, which was presumably a small "miners' dry" where mine clothes were left to dry overnight.

To the east and north of the buildings, part of the ore-dressing floor (Fig. 5:P) is in the process of being excavated (Fig. 9).

The original 1847 kerbed floor has a compacted gravel surface where wheelbarrow ruts could be seen when first uncovered. Wooden processing equipment is long gone but associated postholes, low stone platforms, a paved area and a slab-lined pit remain (Fig. 10). Some of these were added

Figure 9: On the dressing floor to the side of the winding house, wheel ruts in tailings were found and recorded, which were probably from a wheelbarrow used to carry part-processed ore. Within days this delicate archaeological survival had been washed away during heavy storms.

Figure 10: Excavations in progress behind the winding house. This platform, with a central stone chute and sump pit, originally had wooden ore processing equipment above. It was a late addition to the dressing floor after its first creation, which left its initial kerb redundant. The adjacent paving was presumably laid because spilled water would have made this part of the dressing floor unacceptably muddy.

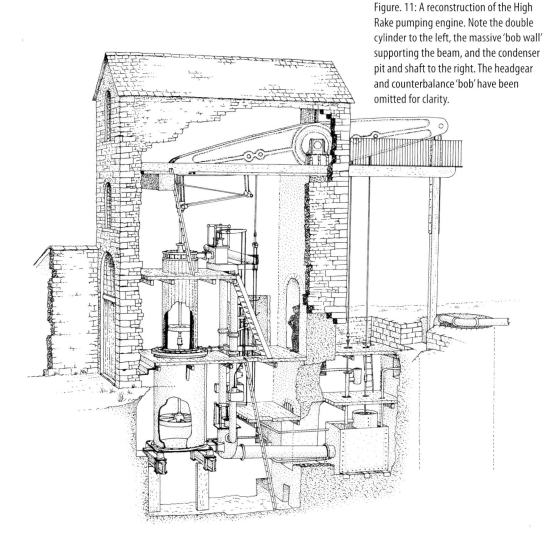

Figure. 11: A reconstruction of the High Rake pumping engine. Note the double cylinder to the left, the massive 'bob wall' supporting the beam, and the condenser pit and shaft to the right. The headgear and counterbalance 'bob' have been omitted for clarity.

behind the winding house after the dressing floor was first created, indicating enlargement and modification to its design.

There are still substantial hillocks of mine waste surrounding the site but they have been moved about during the reworking in the 20th Century. Little remains of the mine office (Fig. 5:Q), which lay to the east in an area used for a rubbish dump and now planted with trees.

From being a lost mine in 2000, much has now been uncovered and a visit to the site is recommended. For your own safety, do not climb walls or railings, the drop into the condenser pit is 26 feet (8m)!

Figures 12 and 13: Two views of the engine pit of the pumping engine house.

The arched opening above gave access to the condenser pit.

The large alcove above is where the lower cylinder stood , with its base at the same level as the ledge.

Further Reading

Barnatt, J. and Vernon, R. (2007) Geophysical survey at Magpie Mine near Sheldon to identify the position of the 1840 winding house and its boiler house. Mining History 16.5, pp. 24-31.

Rieuwerts, J. H. (1964) High Rake lead mine, Windmill. Bulletin of the Peak District Mines Historical Society 2.4, pp. 175-8.

Willies, L. (1979) Technological development in Derbyshire lead mining 1700-1880. Bulletin of the Peak District Mines Historical Society 7.3, pp. 117-51.

Willies, L. (1983) The Barker family and Wyatt lead mining businesses, 1730-1875. Bulletin of the Peak District Mines Historical Society 8.6, pp. 331-68.

Willies, L., Rieuwerts, J. H. and Flindall, R. (1977) Wind, water and steam engines on Derbyshire lead mines: a list. Bulletin of the Peak District Mines Historical Society 6.6, pp. 303-20.

Acknowledgements

John Barnatt would like to thanks the members of the PDMHS Conservation Team who for the last seven years have given generously of their time to bring High Rake Mine back to life; he has written the account of the mine on their behalf. Many people have helped over the years, but amongst the stalwarts who deserve special mention are Keith Gregory, Chris Heathcote, Phil Shaw, Paul Smith, Dave Williams, Brian Woodall, Terry Worthington and Dave Wright. Figure 13 was drawn by John Barnatt from a computer generated three-dimentional engineers drawing by John Thorpe. Advice on the mine archives has been given by Dr JH Rieuwerts. Sheffield Archives, The Trustees of the Chatsworth Settlement and John Goodchild kindly allowed access to historic documents. Don Mitchell did the initial surveying for overall site plan. Many local people have shown continued interest in the project, giving information, encouragement and practical help, with particular mention of Sheila Martin and Bob Campbell from Windmill, and Dennis Collier of Poyntoncross Farm. The Peak District National Park Authority, who own the site, allowed the project to take place and gave support throughout. They, together with The Vision Project, The Sustainability Development Fund and Derbyshire County Council gave grants to provide on-site interpretation and safety measures.

The excavated coal-yard at High Rake mine. The pumping steam engines were hungry beasts and a good store of coal was necessary to feed them. The coal was brought from Dronfield and in winter when pumping at the mine was most needed a large stockpile was particularly important in case the coal wagons could not get through.

A recently rediscovered glass plate of the ruined engine house of High Rake Mine photographed at some time in the late 19th or early in 20th Century before it was eventually demolished.

6. The Great Hucklow Liberty

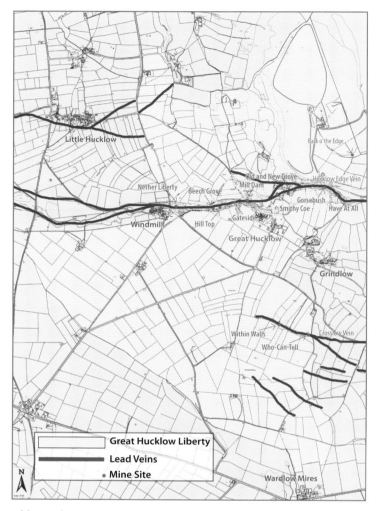

The Great Hucklow Liberty extended from the Bradwell Road through Hucklow village and woods until shortly before the Abney Road junction. All its mines irrespective of their differing geological problems were dominated by the necessity of draining (unwatering) the levels once they had passed below the water table.

In the first section of the Liberty from the Bradwell Road to Mill Dam Mine the rake is similar to that in Little Hucklow with natural cavities occurring in the limestone ('shakey'). Although there were at least three swallows in this area to aid the drainage none of them were sufficiently deep or efficient to dispose of the water from the deeper levels. Unfortunately lack of finance meant that the agreement of 1766 to drive an ambitious

drainage sough from Cow Pasture Mine was never completed. A similar fate may have befallen the agreement referred to in August 1671 in the Barmote collection. This was between Garden End Grove (also known as Nalls Grove) and Hill Top Mine and nearby mines Bramwell Grove, Andrew Grove, Cleaton Grove, Swanne Grove, Ashtons Grove and a half meer called Primgap Grove to share the costs of mutual drainage being 'much troubled with water'.

This section of the Liberty seems to have been the first area to be mined in the Liberty and the names of many groves or mines are redolent of the early free miners, many of whose mines have long since vanished.

By the nineteenth century the smaller mines

Copy of Document in the possession of Lord Houghton taken July 1878 of –

The Preambulation of Boundaries of the Lordship of Great Hucklow as followeth. First beginning at Little Dowse Hole straight following the East end of Woodroufe close to Jackcross Gate so down Jackcross Lane to Within Wall so passing the Highway eastward down the wall unto the bottom of Grindlow Dale so straight down the bottom of Grindlow Dale unto Silidale Acer so straight down the middle of Silidale Acer unto Silidale Sich so down Silidale Sich unto a Great Stone in Wardlow Myers so turning up the Great Sich in Wardlow Myers unto Stanley Moor Nooke so straight up the Dale unto Thicker so taking in the Thicker so straight up Hucklow Slack unto certain pits in the Road of the Slack called Bilberrie Pits so straight up the Heath to Pointon Cross so turning down the Carrier Gates Eastward unto Gate so down the Lane North Tunsfurlong Barn only leaving out Great Tunsfurlong and Hoppdale Knowes so straight on the Lane to Hazlebadge Lordship so turning eastward down after Hazlebadge unto Brownhill Dale so turning Southward up after the Brook unto White Lee and so turning Eastward up after Hazlebadge Lordship unto Hazlebadge Wood and so unto Rissin Lake so turning down the midst of Rissin Lake unto the Bottom of Hucklow Brook so following straight after the Great Ditch which parteth Hucklow and Grindlow and so unto Hucklow Edge after the ring fence betwixt Hucklow and Grindlow unto Dowse House so taking in Dowse House and the yard unto Little Dowse Holes –

Above, the transcription of a 'Preambulation' made along the boundary of the Great Hucklow Liberty taken in July 1878.
(reproduced by kind permission of the Shuttleworth family)

in this area were consolidated into the bigger concerns of Nether Liberty, Watch and Ward, Hill Top / Beech Grove and Gateside. But by the middle of the century the early cooperation had given way to bitter rivalry which resulted in battles in the mines themselves and then in the courts. The problems encountered once the miners had reached the toadstone at about a depth of 440 feet eventually defeated the Great Hucklow Mining Company formed from Hill Top Mine, Beech Grove Mine and Watch and Ward Mine.

Mill Dam Mine marks the beginning of the shale bed which covered the limestone from there onwards as far as Eyam; at Mill Dam the shale was only about 51 feet in depth but at Have At All Mine the miners had to penetrate 252 feet before they could reach the limestone which contained the lead ore. The shale presented a different set of problems. This is probably why the miners do not seem to have explored this area before the 1650s. The miners drove shale gate soughs (tunnels) into the hill side to locate the vein-bearing limestone which then doubled up as drainage soughs or pumpways. The water would be hauled up in leather buckets to the level of the sough and then discharged into it. The soughs driven for Old and

New Edge Mine about 1670 - 1695 are probably some of the earliest of this kind.

The mines to the east of Mill Dam are distinguished by their early success and remarkable cooperation largely because the gentlemen adventurers became involved at an early stage and the mines shared many of the same owners and shareholders. Many of the mines to the west, however, especially in the Little Hucklow Liberty, were worked even before the early 1600s by free miners. The wealthier landowners or adventurers only took over in the following century or later. From the end of the eighteenth century all the mines suffered from the fall in the price of lead. In addition most of the lead ore was exhausted at the levels which the miners had reached. To drive deeper would mean risking much more expense and further drainage problems. There are no records of any of the mines in the Hucklow Liberty east of Mill Dam using steam power, unlike Mill Dam Mine itself and its more prosperous rivals.

Nether Liberty Mine

The Nether Liberty Mine straddled the two liberties of Little and Great Hucklow. On a map of 1892 held in the Chatsworth archives the mine is shown both east and west of the Bradwell road. If, as Dr JH Rieuwerts suspects, the mine referred to as the Nether Groove Mine at Windmill is in fact Nether Liberty then we know that it was working by 1669 when a case for alleged trespass was brought by neighbouring miners. We know too that Richard Bagshaw of Castleton owned a share in the mine, but the amount of ore raised seems very small and work was stopped in 1715.

The swallow beneath Nether Liberty seems to have given the mine its importance. It was 234 feet below the surface and an agreement was signed in 1766 with the partners of Cow Pasture Mine in the Little Hucklow Liberty to drive east towards Nether Liberty Mine from a swallow in their mine which was at a deeper level than that at Nether Liberty. The intention was eventually to unwater or drain all the mines from as far as Smithy Coe. Unfortunately, as with so many of the drainage schemes, the adit (drainage tunnel) did not even reach as far as Hill Top mine; presumably the owners were defeated by lack of finance. The accounts of Mrs Mary Rodes, a descendant of William Bagshawe of Hucklow Hall, show how the scheme was a toll on the mine's finances.

The mine is mentioned in the reckonings of Mary Rodes' grandfather, Aymer Rich, in 1744 and again in March and June 1751 when six workmen were sinking four fathoms in an engine shaft and sinking a sump in an old vein to eight fathoms. Mrs Rodes accounts 1770 show the mine made an overall profit of £38 17s 7d for six months to September 30th. It was certainly in production in 1792 as the Barmaster accounts for a three-month period state that at the end of Lady Day 8.5 loads of ore were measured at Nether Liberty. Up to this time the mine was owned by the descendents of William Bagshaw.

Thirty-five years later it was still in operation with a William Oldfield mining ore of 1 load 3 dishes on October 13th 1827 and the same being brought for measuring by a Thomas Hill. On the 23rd October 1827 a George Gregory sold belland to Benjamin Wyatt, a mine agent: 22 loads 6 dishes.

For the following year 1828 a total of 49 loads 4 dishes of belland and some 39 loads 6 dishes of ore were extracted over twelve months, William Oldfield mining the ore while Rebecca Oldfield processed the belland. It is not uncommon for a whole family to be involved in mining activities as the Oldfields were here. Hugh helped out at Nether Liberty but also worked ore at Who Can Tell, while Elias was busy finding belland at Washers mine.

By 1842 William Gregory and Thomas Bagshaw, or more likely their employees, had hillocked some 34 loads 3 dishes over a three month period April to June.

Once processing belland and hillocking, both labour intensive, became the principle source of ore it was a good indication that the bing or pure galena was almost exhausted and the financial viability of the mine was in doubt unless new veins could be found. In the 1970s a shaft opened up on the edge of the Bradwell road which was too dangerous to descend but the sound of running water could be heard below. The same shaft

Making repairs to the void created by the collapsed shaft at the side of the Bradwell Road in 1998.

The covered shaft at Beech Grove Mine – Jack Binks giving a talk.

opened up again in 1998 after very heavy rainfall creating a large hole in the road much to the council engineer's amazement . It almost certainly belonged to Nether Liberty Mine.

The mines between the Nether Liberty Mine and Mill Dam Mine

The western end of Great Hucklow from the end house to the Bradwell road at Windmill had numerous mines and shafts. The mines of note are Beech Grove, Hilltop and Gateside, but there were many more which riddled the land either side of the Rake Road no doubt stretching back to before records were made: Watch & Ward, Kill Tom, Maltby's Venture, Needham's Shaft to name but a few; many were named after their owners.

Following from east to west Watch and Ward Mine is the first mine to be situated completely within the Great Hucklow Liberty. It lies beneath the flat area of land to the north of the rake road which was subsequently quarried and then became a council tip and is now an area of grass and scrub. Little is known of it except that it was worked by the Great Hucklow Mining Company in the nineteenth century.

Beech Grove and Hill Top Mines

Much more is known about Beech Grove and Hill Top mines which lie to the south of the Rake Road. The land here was cleared of hillocks in the last century but a few of the many shafts can still be identified.

The vein at this point divides into four different stickings or ribs of ore often separated by quite narrow bands of limestone which helps to account for the number of mines and shafts marked on the old maps in the Bagshawe Collection. It also explains why it was relatively easy for miners to break through intentionally or by accident into levels or passages already freed, that is claimed, by another mine as in the case of Turner versus Blackwell (page 72)

Hill Top was probably the first mine to be worked in the Great Hucklow Liberty. It is thought to have been worked from the beginning of the seventeenth century and is said to have reached the water table by 1650. In the nineteenth century a find was made of coins dating from 1605-1680 with tools, drinking vessels and tokens dated 1667. The tools included several spades of oak tipped with iron, resembling Roman spades.

On the border of the tree topped hillocks to the south of the Rake Road is a wall running parallel with the road where an indentation in the wall, which is now very difficult to identify, indicates a gin race (track) or a shaft. A hollow on the north side of the wall is Hill Top gin shaft, Ann Turner's shaft of the 1840s. Beech Grove shaft is much easier to find, well capped with concrete blocks lying between the wall and the road, north of Ann Turner's shaft.

Gateside Mine is further along the present road towards the village of Great Hucklow and its capped shaft is surrounded with a fence. Most of our knowledge of this mine is derived from documents of neighbouring mines.

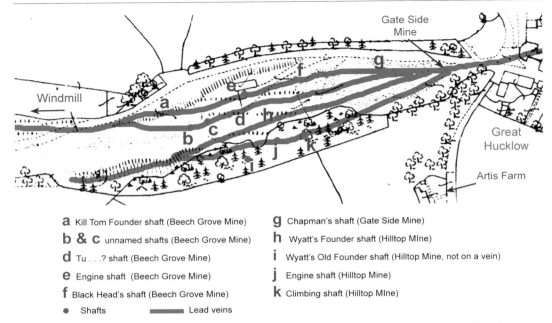

a Kill Tom Founder shaft (Beech Grove Mine)

b & c unnamed shafts (Beech Grove Mine)

d Tu . . .? shaft (Beech Grove Mine)

e Engine shaft (Beech Grove Mine)

f Black Head's shaft (Beech Grove Mine)

● Shafts

g Chapman's shaft (Gate Side Mine)

h Wyatt's Founder shaft (Hilltop Mine)

i Wyatt's Old Founder shaft (Hilltop Mine, not on a vein)

j Engine shaft (Hilltop Mine)

k Climbing shaft (Hilltop Mine)

▬▬▬ Lead veins

The detail above is taken from a sketch map included by Martin Critchley in his survey of Little Mill Dam Mine (PDMHS Bulletin, Vol 6 No 2, May 1977), itself based on maps in the Bagshawe Collection. It shows how the main vein divides into 'stickings' containing lead ore with narrow bands of non-mineralised material (riders) between them. It helps explain how easy it was underground for miners to break through into an area already freed and claimed by another mine, whether on purpose or inadvertently, and why there were so many shafts in such a relatively small area.

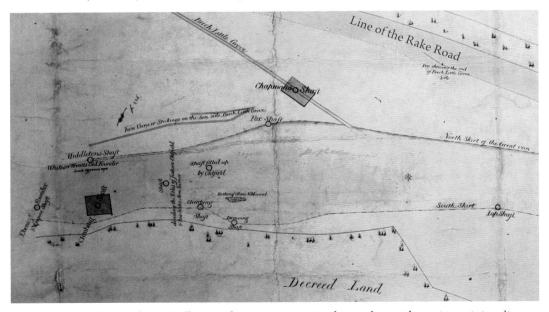

Part of a plan in the Bagshawe Collection drawn up in 1842 to be used as evidence in a mining dispute concerning Joshua Oldfield, brother of Ann Turner, over the title of Gateside Mine. It shows details of some of the main features of Hilltop and Gateside mines and the dividing line between the two. Note the area described as 'Decreed Land' which featured in the legal actions of Mary Rodes. The course of the 'Great Vein' is tinted blue, and the square shapes indicate shafts enclosed by coes.

The swallow which served these mines is said to be beneath the plantation or group of trees on the opposite side of the road and is marked roughly in this area on a map of 1860. Its depth is about 240-250 feet below the surface which means it was too high to drain the mines once the miners had driven below this level which then necessitated some form of pumping. Hence the agreement with Cow Pasture Mine in 1766 to drive a level from their deeper swallow to Nether Liberty swallow and on to the plantation swallow and even through to Smithy Coe Mine to improve the drainage for all the mines bordering the Rake Road. But like so many of the more ambitious drainage projects of that era it was never completed.

Mary Rodes v Joshua Needham 1787: Hill Top Mine

Several case histories provide an interesting insight into the bitter disputes which raged either over water drainage or ownership of mineral rights. In 1787 Mary Rodes took Joshua Needham to court. He was the Barmaster but had worked for Mary for some four years as superintendent of Hill Top Mine and received a salary to act as her agent to collect and receive certain duties of lead ore. Mary maintained that parcels of land owned by her were not subject to mineral laws and customs, that is, they were 'decreed lands' and therefore exempt from the duties usually paid to the Kingsfield and she could demand the payment of lot and cope to herself on lead so mined. She accused Joshua of measuring some 500 cartloads of lead ore valued at £500 for which she had demanded payment of 'Lot and Cope'. Joshua had refused and therefore had neglected his duty to her.

Mary Rodes assumed she had the right of 'Lot and Cope' because she had previously taken persons to court in 1785 (Rodes v Dicken) for actions of trespass on decreed land and won her case.

In this case Joseph Dicken at William Blackers Yard and Thomas Hall junior and Thomas Longden worked Nalls Yard (also known as Hill Top) on land belonging to Mary Rodes. The ore had been measured by Joshua Needham as Barmaster. Needham was in rather an ambiguous position; as Barmaster on the one hand and Mary's employee as agent on the other.

As plaintiff she had admitted that the lands at Great Hucklow came under the Kingsfield along with newly enclosed areas but that the land in question was old enclosed land and not subject to the mineral laws and customs. In the list of mine owners there is mention of decreed land of 5 meers owned by Aymer Rich, whose interests Mary had inherited on his death.

In evidence she referred to the court of James 1st 1618. By decree it was accepted that the King and his lessee had rights in waste ground and freeholder lands other than in ancient lands of Sir William Cavendish, Ellis Furneys and John Hill. Certainly her ancestor William Bagshawe had obtained decreed land from William Cavendish in 1657. Mary, however, never proved that the yards in her dispute were part of these ancient lands. Instead she produced several licences granted by the plaintiff and her ancestors to persons to work lead mines in several parts of her land in Hucklow from which she had received a part of the lead ore produced.

Upon that basis Mary Rodes considered she had rights:

to all the lot & cope duties given to the lessee
to all the ore so mined by the miners

and maintained that Mr Needham was also liable in allowing the miners to carry away the ore to be measured by the Barmaster.

Joshua Needham was, however, backed by the Duke of Devonshire as Lessee of the Kingsfield who could not afford to allow Mary Rodes to win as this would mean that he was deprived of the duties of lot and cope for the ore which had been mined on her land. He feared it would constitute a precedent if Mary Rodes won her case and other miners would be demanding the right not to pay duty. Inevitably Mary Rodes lost her case this time.

Previously Mary Rodes' ancestor, William Bagshaw, owner of Mill Dam Mine, had also been in dispute with the Crown in 1679, citing a decree from the time of King John which exempted him from paying the duties of Lot and Cope since his land lay within an ancient freehold, that is it was 'decreed land.'

There is mention in other documents that Smithy Coe, Gateside and Mill Dam were also on decreed land so possibly the fact that the Duke of

Collection of old mining tools found at Hill Top Mine. including a wisket, a kibble, bucking irons and iron shoes for wooden spades.

Devonshire won the case may have pre-empted any further disputes. As late as April 1909 James Bagshaw of Grindlow was declaring he held decreed land in an auction of some of his lands at Great Hucklow and Grindlow.

After Mary Rodes death it seems that most of the land of the Bagshawe estate was sold to solicitors Rimington and Wake. Mr B Wake however, seems to have been the beneficiary of this deal but it is very unclear who came to own the mineral rights and the mines.

Turner v Blackwell: Hill Top and Beech Grove – Mines at war 1847

The distressing case of the Blackwell brothers and Ann Turner, sister of a Joshua Oldfield who owned a shaft somewhere within the Gateside Mine title, illustrates the rivalry between the mines especially when their workings were so close to each other and the extent to which mine owners would go to win their case.

Ann Turner, recently widowed and having been left her husband's estate including Hill Top Mine, decided in 1845 to go into partnership with a Joseph H Taylor, owner of Gateside Mine - a surgeon from Bradwell.

For two years all was well. However, on Monday 4th June 1847, whether intentionally or not, a group of miners from Beech Grove invaded her workings. Throughout the following year there were protracted proceedings between Ann and the owners of Beech Grove. The Blackwell brothers, James and Thomas, were fined on several occasions by the Barmote Court for trespass: on January 19th a £12 fine and in March another fine of £20.

The description of the fracas which gave rise to the court case is worth quoting from Nellie Kirkham's account:

'A gate was to be driven east towards Gateside Mine at joint expense, and directly it reached this mine it was to be Taylor's charge. If either mine ceased to be worked, it was not to pay any of the expenses of working the gin.

The first episode in the documents occurred on Monday January 4th, 1847, when Robert Howe, miner and mine agent to Ann Turner, went down Hill Top Mine with William Bagshawe. Their shift was from 4pm in the afternoon until about 10pm and Howe heard a noise like someone cutting through, so he *'staid to see what it was if anybody should break thro' to us'*, and by 1am on the Tuesday a hole had been cut through from Beech Grove workings in to Hill Top workings, *'not large enough for a body-gate'*, but large enough for *'tobacco smoke and a smell of malt liquor'* to come through. The hole was then enlarged enough for Howe to see through it Thomas Hilton and two Bradwells, men employed by Blackwell in Beech Little Grove. Between 2–3am a hole large enough for a body-gate had been blasted, and in Beech Little Grove miners could be heard eating and drinking and calling out to each other, *'sup again lads … we'll drive them out'*, and shouting to the Hill Top men, *'We'll make you go out whether it's ours or not we'll have the spot!'*

At the last shot of the blasting, one of the Bradwells called out *'Here's a shot going – stand out of the road.'*

By this time William and Benjamin Turner, Sam Bray, and other Hill Top men of the next shift had come down the mine. The Hill Top men moved back into safe places, but it turned out to be a sham shot, being only a straw filled with gunpowder, and while this was going off, the Beech Grove men rushed through the hole into Hill Top Mine. William Frost, miner, and part-proprietor of Beech Grove, rushed at Howe, shouting, *'We'll make you go out whether it's ours or not'.*

With the scuffle all the candles went out except one, and Frost seized Howe, cutting and bruising his head, and tearing his grove-shirt sleeve nearly off, and pulling his arm until it nearly disabled him and his strength went. Frost also struck at Howe's candle with an auger and hit his hand. In the darkness someone punched him so that he later said he could not turn over in bed for several nights afterwards. He was so exhausted by his injuries that he lay in the wagon gate, over two hundred feet below the surface, for half an hour before he could climb up the climbing shaft to the surface.'

On one occasion the mine and all its contents were arrested. Not only had the brothers tried to take over Ann's workings but they had also started to obstruct their pathways. Looked at from the Blackwell brothers point of view they may appear to have had just cause for their invasion, since Hill Top had driven crosscuts between the two mines.

Obviously the pair felt they had a strong case because they made representation at the Chancery Court in London. Ann Turner, now penniless, was arrested for contempt of court for non-appearance and failure to pay the cost of an arbitration award.

Ann may well have failed to see why she should pay up if the Blackwell brothers had refused to pay any of their fines. However, the Court of Chancery takes precedence over the Barmote Court and had to be respected.

By 1849 Ann Turner was therefore in Derby gaol for insolvency debts. She had incurred a number of legal expenses through her continued pursuit of her rights through the Barmote Courts and the Blackwells' failure to pay their fines; she had borrowed a total £1002 from local people and owed a £1000 to her attorney. The constant battles with the brothers took their toll on her other activities as a farmer and butter dealer. The loss of her house must have been the final blow. The life estate left to her by her husband had been mortgaged to Mr Wake, a solicitor from Sheffield, who had acquired most of the surface land from the Bagshaw's Hucklow estate and features as the landowner in a case described below (Wake v. Houghton and Wake v Hall p64). Unable to pay the rent due Ann lost all her 'effects' and the last we hear of her is in the debtor's goal.

To what extent Ann was a victim of a male dominated society is difficult to assess. It was not unknown for women to own mines and go down them. Determined as she was, Ann may have been ill-advised with little appreciation of the workings of the higher courts or financial affairs and could not afford legal advice at the end when she most needed it.

The Great Hucklow Mining Company

Exactly what happened to Hill Top Mine after Ann's imprisonment is unclear, but Hill Top and Beech Grove became one and formed part of the Great Hucklow Mining Company with the lower part of Nether Liberty Mine and all of Watch & Ward, with Thomas Hall as the agent. Gateside came under the Mill Dam Mining Company as well as Smithy Coe below 300 feet.

From a map section drawn about 22yds from Hill Top shaft, dated about 1860, it appears that the vein worked by Hill Top joined the Beech Grove vein just above the 'gate' that led to the swallow they both used, which would help to account for the fact that a map of the Great Hucklow Co. shows Beech Grove as its principal mine.

Great Hucklow Mining Company v Mill Dam Mining Company

Water remained a problem for all the mines but the rivalry between the Great Hucklow Mining company and the Mill Dam Mining Co. prevented them from reaching a sensible and amicable solution.

Between the 1850s and 60s production boomed. By the end of the decade Hill Top / Beech Grove was equipped with steam- powered engines. There are records in the Derbyshire Records Office to the supply of a fly wheel and boiler in 1855 and in 1859 in the Mining Journal to a 14 horse power engine and later in 1862 to the fact that the company is pumping from 75-80 fathoms. In 1863 a new boiler may have been supplied by Omerod & Co. Manchester for £176 .. 13 .. 0.

The Great Hucklow Mining Company used the plantation swallow to drain Hilltop and Beech

Grove Mines but in the 1850s some of the drainage water appeared to seep back to Gateside Mine (under Mill Dam management). This caused a rift as, according to Nellie Kirkham, the gin pumps of Mill Dam Mining Company ended up lifting the water of both companies especially when Great Hucklow Mining Company closed access to its swallow. A gin could refer to any type of engine, but this engine was probably still powered by three or four horses, eventually replaced by a steam powered engine in 1859. The pump would not have lifted the water to the surface but to a level which joined the pumping shaft from where it could normally flow into a sough or swallow. How it lifted the water is again in doubt, whether by kibbles (leather buckets) or by some sort of hydraulic system. In Mill Dam it appears the water had nowhere to go once the swallow was closed.

In return for the closure of the swallow access Mill Dam Mining Company installed an iron door to prevent water from Great Hucklow Mining Company returning to them and in addition turned other waters in their mine along a level with the intention of flooding Hilltop. Such action caused problems for both mines as neither could relieve themselves of water until one or both companies gave way or came to a sensible compromise. Neither side was prepared to do this and inevitably the underground war ended up in the law courts (see Mill Dam Mine p 64).

The Great Hucklow Mining Company sank a shaft at Hill Top between 1872-3 to a depth of 600feet, 150 feet deeper than their rival the Mill Dam Company, but still failed to penetrate the toadstone which they had first reached in 1864 at about 438-50 feet. This according to the mine agent William Chapman's notes *completely upset the mine, no attempt is at present made to sink it through* (Jan 12th 1872). By June 1873 the pump trees and rods had been raised from the shaft and soon afterwards the engine house and boiler house were demolished. Another mine had been defeated by difficulties presented by the toadstone.

The repercussions of the closure of The Great Hucklow Mining Company, Wake v Houghton 1878

This court case arose five years after The Great Hucklow Mining Co. closed in 1873 and must have concerned what remained of Hilltop and Beech Grove mines.

In 1878 in the High Court of Justice Exchequer Division, William & Bernard Wake, solicitors of Sheffield, but also owners of the estate and interests at Hucklow Hall and adjoining lands, filed for damages against Lord Houghton & others. Richard Monkton Milne Houghton, Baron of Frystone Hall, Ferrybridge Yorks, a poet (and suitor, no less, of Florence Nightingale until rejected) was related to Mary Rodes. From Mary he had apparently inherited mineral rights, presumably the decreed land in the case of Rodes v Needham 1787 which had not been sold to Rimington and Wake in 1809. Along with John Spencer Ashton Shuttleworth and John Hancock, Lord Houghton was served a writ of summons on the 15th July:

'for damages for wrongfully entering and trespassing upon Plaintiffs land at Great Hucklow carrying on divers mining and other operations therein and thereon and for carrying away divers minerals, trees and other matters therefrom and wrongly depriving the Plaintiff of their goods namely minerals, calk, feagh spa,r timber and other matters and for an injunction.'

The Wakes sought damages of some £10,000 and a perpetual injunction restraining the defendants. Seven months later, however, the case is emended to Wake & other v Hall & other at the Derbyshire Winter Assizes on the 15th February 1879. It is not clear whether Lord Houghton and others held the mineral rights of the land in question whilst Mr Hall, who had been manager of the mine when it was working, and others had leased the mine or just carried out the actual operations. Reference is made to *spot in question which is called sometimes Hill Top and sometimes Beech Grove*.

Since the land in question includes both Hill Top and Beech Grove Mines it could be that Houghton and Wake owned a section each. The case became very protracted and several case histories were called upon to provide evidence before judgement was finally awarded on Point 1 to the Plaintiffs – the right to recover possession of a mine when mining is finished, and on Point 2 in favour of the Defendants' rights to conclude their business without trespass. The Plaintiffs had claimed damages for trespass as mining had finished and the miners had remained on site presumably to salvage what they could from the hillocks, gear and buildings. However, the 5th custom of the Mining Laws gave exclusive rights to the miner whilst the mine was being worked, but did not state the case for the miner when work had finished. Would he become a trespasser if he did not vacate the site immediately? Needless to say, both parties appealed and in the event the Judges dismissed both appeals with costs.

This aerial view of Gt Hucklow village appears to have been taken some time in the 1950s: the new Sycamore House (6) was built late 40s and the Unitarian Holiday Homes (1) demolished in the early 60s, and the Playhouse (3) is in its post 50s state. There are no houses on the Green (5) and there is no Artis Cottage (built 1968).

The spoil heaps from both Mill Dam Mine and Smithy Coe mine can be clearly seen (4 & 2), and it is just possible to discern the hillocks on the Beech Grove Mine site along the road out to Windmill (7). Beyond Windmill the High Rake hillocks (8) are still bare of trees.

7. Mill Dam Mine

| Mill Dam House – originally the mine offices and weighbridge | Burr Tor Farm House – built with the stone from the demolished Mill Dam Mine chimney | Winding engine house (whimsey) | Blacksmith's Shop | Village School | Man-powered capstan (for hauling heavy wooden pump rods) |

The above composite picture of the Mill Dam Mine site is made from three photographs, taken between about 1895 and the 1920s, which we have combined to give an idea of the layout of the original buildings and a feel of the landscape of the time. The right hand half of the picture is from the photograph we have of the remaining mine buildings taken before 1896 when it is recorded that the headframe and its associated gear were dismantled. We know also that the last engine to be installed at the mine was of the Cornish type, so it is likely that the beam was still in place (just visible beneath the wooden railed platform) with its associated pumping rods. The engine and its gear were dismantled and removed early in the 20th Century.

Mill Dam House was formally the weighbridge and offices of the mine, and it is possible still to discern the line of the arch round the centre door where the trucks entered to be weighed.

The site of the main shaft was in the present garden of Bank Cottage and was used for both pumping and winding. The rear wing of Bank Cottage was the boiler house for the pumping engine, served by a chimney since demolished. The engine house, itself, also demolished, stood in front of these. When Bank Cottage was recently renovated a climbing shaft was found beneath the floor of its dining room.

To the right of the Mill Dam House is a stone shed which housed a small steam powered winding engine or whimsey. On the east wall of the shed it is just possible to make out the marks of the winding drum, and in the garden there was once evidence of the chimney, now demolished. Before the installation of steam engines there would have been a gin engine powered by horses

The building to the right of the stone shed housed the blacksmith who was important for making and repairing the miners' tools and equipment. The great grandson of one of the blacksmiths still lives in the village.

Gable of cupola building – later converted into the Playhouse

Headframe and winding wheel

Pulley wheel for handling the wooden pump rods

Beam of Cornish steam pumping engine

Engine house

Chimney flue for the steam engine

Buildings, now the modern Bank Cottage

The roofed man-powered capstan to the left of the headframe would be used for hauling the heavy wooden pump rods attached to the beam of the engine.

Behind the headframe is the gable end of what was part of the buildings used for lead smelting until at least 1891; this building was later used for agricultural purposes before it was converted into the Playhouse Theatre in 1938. The theatre closed in the early 1970s and was sold on to the Sheffield Scouts Association as an outdoor pursuits centre which later became the Foundry Adventure Centre.

In the background of the photographs you can see the extensive hillocks of waste material from the mines. Stone from the demolished engine chimney was used to build Burr Tor farm house.

The colour photograph above shows the equivalent modern view of part of the site.

Mill Dam Mine is the flagship mine of Great Hucklow: set in the heart of the village it is a mine with which the village is familiar even today from the old photograph featured on the previous page. Many of the buildings shown on the photograph still remain, even if somewhat transformed. Through the ages Mill Dam Mine has had many highs and lows with a succession of owners vying with each other over title and possession, water rights and drainage. All were at the mercy of the natural hazards of underground working and the fluctuations of market prices as the mines still are today. Moreover, the new Mill Dam Mine, which was opened in 1987, closed again in 1999 and at the time of writing is about to reopen, is a modern example of the vicissitudes of the mining industry.

Mill Dam Mine 1600s - 1855

Although written evidence for the working of Mill Dam Mine is scarce before the 1850s there is compelling evidence of underground mining activity as far back as the early 1600s. The depth of the shale covering is only about 51 feet above the limestone and does not appear to have deterred the miners from exploiting the rich vein of galena until they reached a depth where draining the water became a problem.

The earliest reference to the mine we have found so far is in 1679 ,when the mine owner of Mill Dam Grove, William Bagshaw, refused to pay his duty of Lot and Cope claiming he had exemption. The mine lay within 'ancient freeholds' or 'free land' which had been granted by King John and was free from Crown duties. A similar claim was also made by Bagshaw's descendent Mary Rodes in1737 in her case against Joshua Needham (see Hill Top Mine).

In the Ann Turner lawsuit of 1845 (see Hill Top mine, Turner versus Blackwell) a Mr John Bainbriggs is mentioned as the owner of Mill Dam Mine, which indicates that it was in use then.

Records for the Mill Dam Mine date from the 1850s when The Mill Dam Mining Company explored the possibilities of opening up the mine to exploit 'the powerful veins' beneath the shale. By then the owners, as at High Rake Mine, could take advantage of the technological advances in engines for pumping and lifting. However, the following agent's report details the poor state of the mine when the company acquired it and bears evidence of its long history.

Report in the *Derbyshire Times* (13th March 1858):

'The main gates and gin-shaft are in most ruinous condition. To put them in order will be attended with considerable expense. I would, therefore, repair only the shafts and climbing gates, and merely keep the others open for ventilation and the under workings of the mine. The top workings in each mine are poor at present, although there are 14 men and four boys working the same on cope, and paying the average sum of seven shillings per load. I have also three men and four boys engaged in cleaning out the under level. Our progress here is slow at present, owing to the air being bad and very pernicious. I am with all possible dispatch driving a rip-gate west of Mill Dam. The ground is very favourable, but not any ore to value: price of driving 30 shillings per fathom. I intend to drive this gate another six fathoms, and then put down a pump. This will not only give ventilation to the level, but will be very useful for other purposes. The Old Man's workmanship in this level is all pick work, and purely an Old Man's cutting. I have not the least doubt it has been driven to the Mill Dam Mine more than 300 years ago, and when emptied of its contents, which is sediment or water-settling, we shall be then able to intersect one of the most promising fields of mineral property.'

The "Old Man", or more colloquially "T'Owd Mon", is an expression used in many English and European mining areas. It refers to early miners who worked in ancient and largely uncharted mines. Some apply it to the ghosts of ancient miners.

The agent added:

'The Hill Top Mine, which adjoins Mill Dam property, and is on the same vein, is very rich, and the profit of the workings since the measure of ore about Christmas last is estimated at something like £1,000. Several of the committee of Mill Dam made a thorough exploration of the works on Wednesday last.'

The report of Doug Nash published in 1969 confirms the evidence that the mine had been worked well before the 19th Century. He explored the underground workings via a shaft called

Cockerfield shaft when he surveyed the mine underground for the OM.M.R.&E.G Project prior to the opening of the new fluorspar mine by Laportes Minerals. Cockerfield Shaft was situated in what had been a coe (a stone shed) on the western edge of the lane to Little Hucklow to the north of the Hucklow vein itself, but within the enclosure of the old Mill Dam Mine. He says:

'Just beyond the raise it is necessary to slide down the debris into undoubtedly "Old Man" workings lower than the preceding level and roofed with stemples and bunnings (staging built of wood capable of holding many tons of waste rock) these now rotten and collapsing – extending as far as I could see.'

In many places rich ribs of ore had largely been removed from the upper parts of the main vein of the ore field by about 1600, often by men working to supplement their livelihoods as farmers. Horatio Bradwell, secretary to the Mill Dam Company in 1880, also confirms this, stating that the ancients had cut out the best but leaving good quality lead ore still in the cheeks of the veins.

The Mill Dam Mining Company

The Mill Dam Mining Company was probably formed in 1855 to invest in one of the most promising fields of mineral property but work does not seem to have begun until 1857.

The old pumping and winding mechanism had to be replaced. Eventually the new Mill Dam Mine had three shafts, a winding, a pumping and a climbing shaft but the winding and pumping shafts were combined as in many mines. It had two chimneys, one for the pumping engine and one for the winding engine.

From the evidence of the old photograph taken soon after the mine's closure we can see the pump and winding shaft was situated at the bottom of what is now the garden of Bank Cottage and the tall building since demolished was the engine house. The rear wing of Bank Cottage would have been the site of the Boiler House served by the Boiler House chimney (again, now demolished).

The small building. almost intact, on the opposite side of the track housed the steam powered winding engine, or whimsey. The markings of the winding drum on its left hand wall have helped the archaeologists confirm the position of the winding wheel and shaft. Local memory recalls that a great number of the original paper records of Mill Dam Mine had been stored here but they were sent for the war effort's paper salvage scheme in the 1940s. There is evidence of a chimney beyond this building in the present garden.

Along the track is the smithy also relatively unscathed. Here it is likely that two ancestors of Mr Kenneth Waterhouse of Artis Farm worked as blacksmiths for Mill Dam Mine.

When Bank Cottage was being recently renovated the builders found what is thought to have been a climbing shaft beneath the dining room floor. Unfortunately this was filled in before lead mining experts could explore it and discover whether the story that beneath the area to the east there is a cavern 'you could near put Tideswell church in' is true! Access shafts were quite common in coes and miners' cottages. Local memory maintains that until the middle of last century access to the upper part of the original cottage was by a vertical ladder fixed to one of the inner walls.

The present Mill Dam House was the old weighbridge and offices of the Company, and the arching around the front door of the house, which you can still make out, was where wagons entered the weighbridge; according to Mr Kenneth Waterhouse there also used to be wooden steps on the eastern gable which led to the mine offices.

There is a frustrating lack of evidence for the type or types of engine installed at Mill Dam Mine. Nellie Kirkham says in a paper for the PDHMS in 1953 that the Mill Dam Mine in the 1850s was lifting water by gin pumps up to a level approximately on the contour of Hill Top swallow which was taking the water from both mines. Dr JH Rieuwerts considers that if this is correct it was powered by three or even four horses. This seems to be confirmed by the agent's report to the Derbyshire times quoted above. It was probably to replace this 'gin pump' that in 1859 a combined pumping, winding and crushing engine of twelve horse power made by Davey Bros. of Sheffield was installed costing £300. Shortly after this, according to the Mining Journal of January 1863, another pumping engine was installed in 1862-3 which was presumably larger to cope with the volume of water. Lynn Willies has found a reference (BSA Coll DRO) to a new boiler bought in 1862-3 for

Mill Dam House early last century still surrounded by spoil heaps from the mine. The upper storey of the building once served as the mine offices with the weigh-bridge below; the original stonework arch through which wagons passed to the weigh-bridge can plainly be seen but now enclosing the front door to the house.

somewhere in Great Hucklow for £176-13-0 from Ormerod and Co. It seems probable therefore that the owners had bought a new boiler for the new engine, unless by chance this boiler was intended for Hill Top Mine or Beech Grove Mine, both of which had steam engines.

In *The Mining Journal* of 1870 tenders were invited by the Mill Dam Mining Co. for the erection of a boiler and engine house for a Cornish Pumping engine but there is no evidence about why this was necessary or that it was ever built. It seems strange that, in the collection of newspaper cuttings among the Shuttleworth papers specific to Mill Dam Mine, of which the family were shareholders, the report of the annual meeting of the company for 1870 makes no mention of a possible new boiler and engine house. The report merely explains why the profits were £1,537 down on the previous high of £7,585 in 1869, attributing the decrease to the flooding of the mine for six weeks at Christmas and adds that 'greater facilities for dressing the boose were urgently needed.'

In the garden of Mill Dam house are the remains of a shaft which Mr Tom Parkes says a relative filled in after it collapsed, and local opinion considers that it could be an old pumping shaft perhaps belonging to operations before 1855.

Mill Dam Mine had constant problems with flooding and disposing of water having no natural 'swallow' or convenient sough to act as a drain. This gave rise to serious disputes with Hill Top and Beech Grove Mine owned by the rival Great Hucklow Mining Company. Both companies were mining the same vein and their levels sometimes connected. In the 1850s Great Hucklow Mining Company closed their Hill Top swallow for some unknown reason and Nellie Kirkham describes the consequences:

'Not only was the connecting level under water, but Mill Dam pumps were lifting the water of both mines. It is not positively stated, but it appears as though their pumps were not sufficiently effective to lift all of the water to the surface and evidently they had no efficient swallow of their own, and they had no sough. Local tradition says that Mill Dam had a swallow underground about where the stream from Burrs Mount sinks; this could be correct, but if so apparently it must have fallen in or become silted up or choked, and by this time was no longer functioning.

'As a result a typical lead mine underground–war started. Mill Dam Mine Company fixed an iron door underground near to their pumping shaft across the westward level to the Hill Top swallow to stop water from the latter mine from coming back to them and pouring into their shaft, as it had done after the way to the (Hill Top) swallow was stopped. Troughs were fixed across Mill Dam pumping shaft which carried the water in them to a short west level, and then turned down an old sump 42 feet deep into the lower level, so that Mill Dam water was now deliberately turned into Hill Top Mine to flood it. This meant that so long as the latter kept their swallow closed their wagon gate (the level along which ore was brought to the foot of the winding shaft) and lower workings were

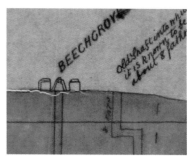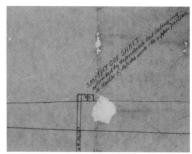

Details from a mine map drawn as evidence during one of the watering disputes. It shows Smithy Coe shaft having a gin winding gear, whilst both Beech Grove and Mill Dam have wheeled headframes. (Bagshawe Collection)

under water. But this also meant that Mill Dam water was not being taken away, and in their mine the water was standing 42 feet above the lower water–gate.

In 1858 the company was forced to find another swallow to drain its mine. Its neighbour to the east was Smithy Coe Mine which had a swallow about 300 feet east of its gin shaft and was reputed to have yet another swallow, but unfortunately the exact position of the two swallows was unknown. However the company acquired the right to work that part of Smithy Coe Mine which was below 300 feet with the intention of extending its workings, already at a depth of 300 feet, eastwards, below the old workings, and locating the swallows. They failed to find the swallows but between 1868 and 1878 the Smithy Coe workings produced over 1000 loads of ore.

Meanwhile the Great Hucklow Mining Company and the Mill Dam Company were at law by November !860 and according to Nellie Kirkham

'the Court of Chancery had ordered an engineer to inspect the latter workings, and he was to be the arbitrator, the award being expected any time. In January 1861 the Mill Dam Company cut into their Sun Vein – the vein crossing the southern part of their ground – and had come across a very rich vein 6 feet wide, producing great quantities of ore, and there were also other good veins.

By March 1861 the right of Mill Dam to pour water into the swallow had been established by the decision of the arbitrator, but there was a threatened further action at law, re the right to use the swallow.

Petherick, a lawyer, on being consulted, found the swallow was situated in the property of the Great Hucklow Mining Company, and that Mill Dam had cut through solid ground to enable their water to reach the swallow, so they had not been following a vein in a mineral manner. Also they had raised the level of this water and caused it to flow into the mines of the Great Hucklow Company.'

An agreement was finally reached between the two companies in 1864 but the problem of drainage had clearly taken its toll on the finances of the Mill Dam Company. From a report in the Derby and Chesterfield Reporter, Nov 21st 1862, we learn that at a shareholders' meeting of the Mill Dam Company the mine had failed to make any money for the last 10 years. The liabilities amounted to £1,780 once all expenses had been paid. The expenses for the year had been £3,310 against £3,193 ore produced and 'nothing has been laid out for new machinery'. 'No dividend had ever been declared but on the contrary many thousands of pounds have been spent on it and the mine is now involved in more debt than at any period since the company was formed'.

A further report of a shareholders' meeting in 1870 shows that there must have been an upturn and 1869 had proved to be their best year when the mine made a total of £7,585 13s 7d. The next year 1870 was not quite so good when it made £6,047 15s 4d. The average weekly yield for 1869 was 121/2 tonnes and for 1870 103/4 tonnes: 'The difference was not caused by any particular failing on the wealth of the workings; the decrease being attributable to the flooding of the mine for 6 weeks at Christmas 1869–70 and to the severe frost which prevented dressing.'

The directors also discussed a proposal that: 'It would be greatly to the advantage of the company if they were placed in a position to smelt their own ores – and having the offer of a smelting mill at a rental within a short distance of the mine – the meeting gave authorisation to the directors to rent the mill'.

The smelting mill in question, or cupola, was certainly not far away, only a matter of yards it seems. In 1874 we have a report of a case at Bakewell County Court of Caleb Heginbotham, a farmer of Great Hucklow (and innkeeper of the Queen's Head), suing the Chairman of the Mill Dam Mining Company for £11 16s 6d for damages to his crops by the fumes issuing from the smelting furnaces of the Company. This said that the smelting works were placed there three years ago (1871). The chimney was 60 feet high and the field of oats was only 50 yards from it. Various witnesses at the case gave graphic accounts of the effect of the smelting. The medical officer of the Sanitary Authority stated that 'Lead was not to be found in the corn but in the soil and in the neighbourhood'. He found a deal of sulphoid of lead on the leaves of the trees in the direction in which the smoke blew, and the water in the neighbourhood was also crusted with the carbonate of lead and the hydrated oxide of lead. He also found sulphoid of lead 'in the turnip tops and foliage of the trees'.

Suffice it to say, Caleb Heginbotham won this case and damages of £11 10s 6d but there appears to have been no sanctions passed on the mine. Moreover the smelting works continued until at least 1891 which seems incredible in this day of health and safety. It was normal however, in the nineteenth century for smelters to be near places of habitation. The west end of the village must have been completely blighted.

There is an interesting agreement made in 1863 between James Flint, a farmer from Tideswell, and the Mill Dam Company 'for the leading of coal from Millers Dale Station to Great Hucklow.' which helps to illustrate how much the whole community must have been involved in the lead business in one way or another.

An undated newspaper cutting from around the 1870s says of the Mill Dam Company, 'during the last month about 80 tonnes have been got. The works still keep good. The 65 fathom level is being opened, and some places will soon be ready for coping', i.e. a contract made with a gang of miners for extracting ore and preparing it for market.

Since the neighbouring mine of Smithy Coe was producing large amounts of lead ore between 1868 and 1878, it may have been a factor in the Company discussing whether to install a new Cornish engine in 1870 in the hopes of unwatering the mine to the same depth as Smithy Coe. The problem of draining the water was never completely solved and eventually the company failed and the mines were closed in 1884.

And so, after consuming much of its shareholders investment, another mining venture which had so much promise came to an end just as at High Rake Mine, except that this time the owners were defeated by lack of drainage and according to Horatio Bradwell 'the poorness of the veins.'

A sad postscript to this era is that according to some villagers who have been down the modern mine, the present day workings have revealed such rich veins of lead ore that they would truly have made the investors a fortune had they had the resources and the technology to overcome the drainage problems at the lower levels. Ironically the modern mine uses the same swallows to drain the mine as did the nineteenth century miners.

After the closure of the Mill Dam Mine

In 1891 Kelly's Directory records 'Mill Dam Mine and Smelting Co; Leonard Maltby manager.' The Maltby family were tenants of Hucklow Hall which was owned by Mrs. B. Wake of Sheffield who was 'Lady of the Manor'. The Maltbys bought the Hall from her in 1921 and sold it to the present owners in 1977. Leonard Maltby is also listed as a farmer in the Kelly's directory so how much mine management and smelting he did is unclear, or when the blight of the smelting works was removed. The mine's head gear was removed between 1895 and 1896 and the shaft collapsed in 1896. Leonard Maltby died in 1897.

Mr William Chapman took over the site as manager, perhaps after Leonard Maltby's death. He supervised the retrieval and grading of the fluorspar from the hillocks and rebuilt Burrs Mount Farm with stone from the demolished mine chimney. In 1872 a William Chapman signs himself as 'agent' in a document in the JH Rieuwerts Collection relating to the Great Hucklow Mining Company. He must have bought the Mill Dam site at some point since he was eventually able to sell the

Members of the Maltby
family outside Hucklow Hall
which was for many years
their family home.

Smelter in 1938. He also transformed the mining offices into the present house known as Mill Dam House which was sold to the Hibbs family and owned by two further families, the Roses and the Mathers until 1986 when Laportes acquired it.

The Parkes family owned the land where Laportes wanted to drive the 'run–in' to the modern mine. This triangle of land alongside Synings Lane included Cockerfield shaft, the shaft which Doug Nash explored in 1969. Tom Parkes thinks that in the 1930's there was an attempt to 'nick' this shaft by Mr E Fisher in order to mine barytes, and his grandfather therefore went down the mine periodically to bring back a small amount of minerals and so establish his ownership in accordance with the ancient mining laws.

When the entrance to the modern mine was built it covered up an ancient shaft from which Tom Parkes remembers as a boy rescuing a run-away dog which had fallen into it – a story quite typical of lead mining areas.

It is fortunate that several of the original Mill Dam Mine buildings still remain, albeit in altered form and purpose, reminding us of the village's historical importance for at least 400 years: part of Bank Cottage the boiler house; the blacksmith's shop; the small building which housed the steam powered winding engine, and Mill Dam House itself still bearing signs of its original purpose as the offices and weighbridge for the mine.

The Chapman Family

The Chapman family were another family involved in the lead industry, not just as miners but in the many trades dependent on the mines.

An early reference to the family is in June 1648 when Edward Chapman, miner from Great Hucklow, appeared as a defence witness to explain the miners' rights in a complicated court case which eventually went as far as the House of Lords. A group of miners, including a group of six from Great Hucklow, were accused of forcible entry on Haddon Fields for attempting to assert their free mining rights there. This was part of the on-going dispute over manorial rights.

What a fund of knowledge of mining law must have been passed down the generations of the Chapman family.

The winding house at High Rake Mine was built in 1843 by William Chapman and Co. and the firm's name appears in similar contexts. William Chapman senior 1810-1881 had interests in Mill Dam Mine and may even have been its agent. Mr William Chapman Jnr. was a wheelwright and blacksmith who worked at Mill Dam Mine and eventually came to buy the building which housed the offices and also the other buildings on the site after the mine's closure. He became manager of the mine site and supervised the retrieval and grading of the fluorspar from the hillocks.

Mr William Chapman was probably the last resident of Great Hucklow who might be regarded as epitomising the spirit and character of the ancient mining traditions. By all accounts he was a fascinating person and we have a glimpse of the man from someone who knew him well – John Mort, Barmaster of the High Peak Hundred Barmote Court. He wrote this piece about William Chapman as one of several short obituary descriptions of his fellow jurymen. He says:

William Chapman of Mill Dam Mine, Great Hucklow. Miner and Juryman with 39 years unbroken service on the jury.

He was on the jury when I first attended a Court in 1905. I well remember my introduction to him and his great zeal in telling me that the old mining customs and traditions of the High Peak were of great value to be remembered and carried on. That they were the people's and belonged to the people. In years later I came to know a great deal more of him.

He was a bachelor and lived alone in a cottage near the Mill Dam Mine. The building was at one time the office belonging to the mine. He knew a great deal about it. His father had some active interest in the mine but Mr Chapman was able to recall many incidents in connection with it. On my rounds I never failed to call on him and if he was at home I would spend an hour listening to him as he wove his time through the past. The measures of ore, the troubles with water and so on.

At the Court he was a creator of joviality. He was a large man with a ruddy complexion and well behaved moustache, a smile always lurking on his features and his familiar appearance never seemed to alter to the last time I saw him at the Barmote Court of 1940. During the period of the War I never had the opportunity to see him again. However, the Court lost in Mr Chapman an individual of great character. He was a man who could tell about his younger days when he and his playmates used to play hide-and-seek under the crinolines of their female parents.

He knew all there was to know about Hucklow, of the past and in his day. When he arrived at the Court there was usually a noisy scene between Winster and Hucklow in the personalities of Albert Marshall and William Chapman.

It is a great pity that John Mort left us no further record of the stories William Chapman told him about Hucklow and of his reminiscences concerning Mill Dam Mine.

He was clearly quite resourceful since he built Burrs Mount from the stone of one of the redundant chimneys and sold it. He then converted the offices and weighbridge into the present house known as Mill Dam House in which he proceeded to live and which was eventually sold to the Hibbs family.

Mr William Chapman

In 1938 he sold the old lead smelting cupola building to Dr L du Garde Peach who transformed it into The Hucklow Playhouse. It seems that William Chapman would have had access not only to many of the documents in the mine offices but also to his father's papers and books. Where these original notebooks are now no one knows. It is known, however, that along with other papers the contents of the offices were collected for the 'War effort' and apparently recycled. William died in the mid 1940s. Some time after the war, Mrs. Rose, the then owner of Mill Dam House is said to have still had a large sack full of papers relating to the mine, but then the trail goes cold.

There is still a 'Chapman House' in the village occupied by William's great nephew, one of a long line of Chapmans, who have lived in it since about 1750 when the family moved from Grindlow. In all the census returns from 1841 to 1891 there is a 'Chapman: Shopkeeper' and part of Chapman House is reputed to have been the shop.

The Cupola Becomes a Playhouse

One of the most significant of the original mine buildings for the recent history of village is that of the barn which served as a store for the lead smelting cupola, the activities of which provoked Mr Caleb Heginbothom into litigation. During the 20s and 30s it was used for storage and agricultural purposes, but in 1938 it was purchased by the Great Hucklow Village Players (founded and led by L du Garde Peach) from Mr William Chapman. The Players had been using part of the barn as storage for their props and scenery used in the productions which had been staged at the Unitarian Holiday Homes during the winter months since 1928.

The Players lost the use of the Homes in 1938 but with a loan from Alderman Graves of Sheffield were able to purchase the barn with the intention of converting it into a small 250-seat theatre. This they achieved in an incredibly short space of time and the first production was mounted in October of that year 'at the time of the full moon'.

Productions continued throughout the War, and afterwards it became a very popular venue for theatre-goers from all parts of the country. At its height the productions were playing for a run of three weeks, twenty-one performances, and to a total audience of over 5,000 people.

The theatre closed in 1971 and was acquired by the Sheffield Scouts Association centre (the deed of sale required that the building should never again be used for theatrical performance). It was later sold to the Sheffield-based Foundry Climbing Centre and became the Foundry Adventure Centre for outdoor pursuits.

Little Mill Dam Mine or Cockerfield Shaft

The shaft of Little Mill Dam Mine, lying due north of the old Mill Dam site and still owned by the Parkes family, is situated on a branch vein of the main Hucklow Edge Vein known as Hucklow Edge North Vein and splits from the main vein just west of the school.

Martin Critchley wrote a report for BPDHMS in 1977 of his survey of Little Mill Dam Mine in which he says the entrance to the shaft was on a hillock overlooking the scrap yard owned by the Parkes family. The area of the scrap yard is now part of the modern Mill Dam mining complex. In 1977 the shaft was still surmounted by a large iron headframe which has since disappeared. The mine was worked by the Mill Dam Mining Company and later by the Parkes family for barytes.

As at Mill Dam the limestone was covered by between 30-35ft of shale. The shaft is 52m.(170ft)

The Mill Dam Mine cupola barn in 1938 during its transformation into the Great Hucklow Playhouse.

The Playhouse in the early 1960s with the building extended to house dressing rooms, scene dock, workshop, and boilerhouse. Note also the spoil heaps from Smithy Coe mine still visible beyond the theatre building. Surviving patrons of the Playhouse may also recognise the tea wagon of the 'Dersert Rat', who provided interval refreshment at the performances, parked at the side of the theatre. The Rover car no doubt belong to L du Garde Peach himself.

The headframe of Little Mill Dam Mine (M Critchley, 1976)

deep and several passages lead off east and west at three different levels; 21.5m(70ft), 38m(124ft), and the foot of the shaft. In his exploration of the mine in 1969 D.A. Nash confirms that there is evidence of T'Owd Mon workings.

Since access to the old Mill Dam Mine workings is no longer possible Martin Critchley's description of the workings of Little Mill Dam Mine gives us a graphic picture of conditions under-ground for the earlier miner. Even if it were still possible to descend the mine the accounts of D.A.Nash and Martin Critchley do not sound very inviting.

In his 1977 report Critchley says:

'The shaft is 52m deep, the top 15m of which is well ginged (lined) with dressed gritstone, supported by a small iron arch on the north wall at the base of the ginging. The remainder of the shaft is sunk through solid rock. Running down the western side of the shaft is a fixed iron ladder . . . (which) ends about 9m from the bottom of the shaft and is attached to wooden stemples (staves) across the shaft. Many of these stemples have rotted through or broken away, giving a strange floating sensation when climbing up the ladder!'

It is not surprising that he recommends future explorers should be 'well lifelined' before descending. He goes on to write:

'At the 38m level passages lead off from the shaft to the east-southeast and the west-northwest.

Access to these levels can be gained by performing various acrobatic activities on the ladder (Electron ladder, not the fixed ladder!) whilst penduluming across the shaft and trying not to collide with the iron counterweight which hangs in the shaft at this level . . . The first part of the (easterly) level is 2m high and 1m wide with a narrow gauge railway track which terminates at the shaft. About 4.5m along the level is the rusting remains of a shovel propped against the left hand wall . . .

The eastwardly level from the foot of the shaft leads off under a not too safe looking stack of deads (waste rock) and immediately opens out into a winze (a shaft connecting two levels) 8m deep in the floor of the passage, which is covered by a rusting iron ladder . . . On the far side of the winze the level continues and access to this may be gained by crawling along an iron ladder over the winze. The passage is very narrow here and leads steeply upwards, which coupled with the loose sandy floor, makes ascent difficult. At the top of the slope the passage widens slightly into a small stope (a vertical fissure where ore had been removed) with a wall of stacked deads at the far end, at the base of which is a shallow winze. The winze is 2m deep with a short upward crawl leading off eastwards at the bottom. This crawl enters a large stope with several passages and a winze in the roof. The stope contains some fine examples of wooden climbing stemples in the upper parts, but access to the winze and other passages in the roof of the rift (crack or opening) has not been possible.'

Following the 60m westerly level from the foot of the shaft Critchley encounters a complex of worked-out passages with well defined horizontal slickensides which sloped slightly to the north-northeast. The passages here were very narrow (0.5m) and on his last visit to the mine in January 1976 this part of it was flooded to the top, which made it impossible to explore further and adds that this was in contrast to the rest of the mine which was very dry.

Critchley's description gives us a taste of the nature of these old working as well as the challenge of their exploration. Parts of the narrow passages driven by the early miners can still be seen in the Modern Mill Dam Mine.

Left, Mill Dam House as it looks today., and to the right is the building which originally housed a small steam powered engine, or whimsey which may have turned a winding drum on the outside of the building, perhaps similar to the one at Magpie Mine, Sheldon (below left).

The small engine house in a detail from an old photograph. One of the figures standing on the spoil heap could be Mr William Chapman. It is said that the house in the background, Burrs Mount, was built by him from stone salvaged from the demolished chimney and engine house of Mill Dam Mine.

The old Mill Dam Mine's blacksmith's shop in the garden of Mill Dam House

The Modern Mill Dam Fluorspar Mine

In 1977 Laporte were investigating the feasibility of opening up Mill Dam Mine to exploit the vein system eastwards principally for fluorspar and negotiated a lease from Leonard Maltby Junior and Ken Parkes (the Parkes had retained rights to Cockerfield shaft) and many other holders of mineral rights along the vein.

The plan to open up the mine again with use of highly mechanised techniques caused a bitter dispute in the village between those in favour of reopening the mine and those against, a dispute which is still vividly remembered today.

Even the modern mine has been subject to the vicissitudes of the market which the story of its opening, closure and current reopening amply illustrates. Ineon, a subsidiary of ICI, acquired the mine in 2008 and with substantial commercial backing is in a position to begin operating it yet again. Even today mine agents and mining solicitors are busy representing their clients who hold the mineral rights of the parts of the vein about to be reopened. If only the old miners could see the driveways and mechanisation of today, yet the same problems still trouble the modern miner – drainage, ventilation, access and above all financial viability.

Fluorspar Extraction at Mill Dam Mine

by John Elkins, former Chief Surveyor for Glebe Mines

The modern Mill Dam Mine was designed to exploit the Hucklow Edge vein system – a major east-west trending deposit of fluorspar, barytes, calcite and lead. The vein was initially worked for lead until 1885, with the old miners largely discarding the other minerals.

Fluorspar, however, was sought as long ago as 1670 when it was used as a flux at Beeley Smelting Mill, and in the 20th Century a demand for higher quality material led to the re-opening of the old Glebe Lead Mine in the village of Eyam.

From 1936 until 1979 the mine workings progressed north to join with Ladywash Mine and then steadily extended 2 km west along the vein system, until the problem of restricted access via a 222 metre deep shaft made them uneconomical.

In 1985 a planning application was made by Laporte Minerals (who had purchased the business in 1959) to the Peak District National Park Authority for a new access at the old Mill Dam Mine site on the edge of the village of Great Hucklow, approximately 2 km further west from where the workings reached in 1979. Consent was granted in 1987 for access via an adit, declining at 1 in 8 to allow the use of modern wheeled machinery which would improve the economic viability of mining. This new access was to be sited within a sunken compound, surrounded by landscaped mounds and connected to the public highway by a private road to avoid lorry traffic in the village.

Following construction of the compound, tunnelling started in late 1987 with the aim of an underground connection as soon as possible with the earlier mine workings from Ladywash, which had ceased in 1979. This would provide for the discharge of underground water via the established drainage system in the old workings, for ventilation and a secondary egress.

Ore production began in 1991, at the point where the 1979 work had ended. The working area steadily advanced along the vein in a westerly direction for a further kilometre, until the closure of Laporte Minerals in 1999.

The company closed because the finished high grade fluorspar from Cavendish Mill could not compete with vast quantities of cheaper material imported from China. The major customer for the fluorspar (a large chemical works on Merseyside) could no longer justify paying Laporte's price and would therefore be using Chinese material.

The assets of Laporte Minerals were sold to Land Regeneration Ltd, a company experienced in tidying and regenerating all types of former industrial sites. However, they quickly realised there was still potential mineral life within the assets. Consequently a small operation was immediately restarted at Cavendish Mill, based upon the more easily-won mineral on Longstone Edge. Unfortunately the mineral from Mill Dam Mine was too expensive to extract so the Mine had to be placed on care and maintenance, with the hope that it would eventually become economically viable.

A new company acquired the assets: Glebe Mines, named after the original mining venture started in 1936. Its future was soon improved when the cheap Chinese fluorspar supplies drastically reduced in the early 21st century. Due to the rapid industrialisation in China more and more fluorspar was used on their home market, and Glebe Mines were able to secure the supply of high grade fluorspar to Merseyside again.

Glebe Mines have just completed a detailed appraisal of the Mill Dam Mine deposit and believe it can again be viable. However, it will require significant investment, which is currently being sourced. The current timetable is for preliminary work to commence at the end of 2007, with ore extraction starting sometime in 2009.

Views of the workings in the modern Mill Dam Mine during the 1990s. Right, work on the face of the main heading, and below, mined mineral being loaded into a dumper truck from a 'slit'. (Paul Deakin)

Postscript

The new investors, INEOS Fluor, are actively preparing to construct a new spiral driveway below ground at Great Hucklow and then to extract ore eastwards towards Silence Mine. Fortunately for the village modern mining methods do not lead to large unsightly spoil heaps and the surface of Silence Heritage site will not be disturbed.

To quote the company's statement:

'This acquisition is important both locally and nationally. It secures the long term sustainability of Glebe Mines as a major employer in the area and supports INEOS Fluor's investment in the UK fluorochemicals industry and the supply of products that are vital for society, which are manufactured at its Runcorn site.'

So Great Hucklow is once again at the forefront of the mining industry. It is only to be hoped that the investors are more successful than some of their predecessors.

8. Mines in the Hucklow Liberty East of Mill Dam Mine

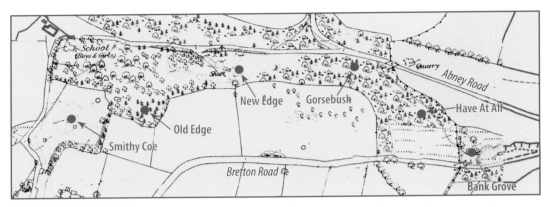

Looking at Great Hucklow School today, set idyllically on the edges of the Hucklow woods, it is difficult to imagine how different the whole aspect would have been when it was first built in 1872. The ancient track known as the 'Holloway' behind the school is the old road from Abney and would have been the main thoroughfare into the village from the north-east. The trees would have long been felled for use in the lead mines which were worked throughout the woods from the seventeenth to the late nineteenth century.

Everywhere there would have been huge spoil heaps (or 'hillocks) which were eventually reworked for fluorspar during the twentieth century. Unfortunately all this subsequent reworking of the ground, a process known as 'hillocking', masked or destroyed much of the remains of the old mines. For most of the twentieth century the school was ringed to the south and east by the heaps which gradually became regenerated by the trees we see today. The heaps to the south were cleared completely only in 1997 when the school playing field was laid out. Some villagers can remember as children playing on these heaps, which also provided a good site for the village bonfire.

The key adventurers on this section of the edge were members of the Bagshawe family, including John Bagshawe of Hucklow Hall, and of the Ashton/Spencer/Shuttleworth family of Hathersage. The papers of both these families have been our main source of information. Initially the families appear to have cooperated with each other. However,

after a court case between the two, costing some £20,000 in 1746, which the Ashton/Spencer family won, it seems that the Bagshawes became less prominent and by the nineteenth century the Shuttleworths appear to have owned all the titles except Smithy Coe. That does not mean that various Bagshawes along with many others did not have shares in the mines. Most investors liked to spread the risks. The minor investors in mine ownership by the nineteenth century included local families such as Ash, Walker and Frost.

The ancient 'Hollow Way' – from Great Hucklow to the Abney Road linked many mines on the Hucklow Vein.

The mines on the eastern stretch of the Hucklow Liberty all encountered the problem of drainage. The ore-bearing limestone could be reached only by shafts penetrating the shale above, at times to a depth of 300 feet, and the water table was comparatively high. JH Rieuwerts considers that Smithy Coe Mine and eventually Old Edge and New Edge Mines were drained from around 1671 by a sough that bypassed the Mill Dam Mine area and discharged directly to the surface in the vicinity of Synings Lane. A swallow features along the same lane on a map of 1850 used at the Chancery Court in the case between Mill Dam Mine and The Great Hucklow Mining Co.

JH Rieuwerts also believes that a swallow in Smithy Coe was cleared by the 1690s which enabled it to receive water from New Edge at a slightly deeper level than the sough. The importance of Smithy Coe seems to lie in its strategic position for the drainage not just of Old Edge and New Edge Mines but even later of Mill Dam Mine. In the 1720s a large sough was begun which was designed to drain all the mines along the Hucklow and Eyam edges into the River Derwent at Stoke Hall – an incredibly ambitious enterprise which had it reached the Hucklow Liberty would have solved the drainage problems of its mines. See the section on Silence Mine for the fuller story.

Nellie Kirkham published a paper in 1963 (BPDHMS Vol 2) in which she recorded the results of her field work and research into the Great Hucklow mines especially those covered in this section. It is thanks to her that we can still find the traces of the mines in woods even though much has disappeared in the last 50 years.

Smithy Coe Mine

Smithy Coe Mine is located to the south of the school and its main shaft, 288 feet deep, may be under the present playing fields. In 1963 Nellie Kirkham records that at Smithy Coe Mine the mounds are dressing hillocks but they have been so much disturbed by hillocking that all features are lost. 'A heap of stones roughly in the centre is supposed to be over the shaft. There is a circular limestone crusher still to be seen' (a wheel for crushing ore). This is corroborated by several of the present villagers but the laying out of the playing fields finally obscured any remains. Mr Kenneth Waterhouse recalls that when the playing fields were laid out an old sough or drain was discovered which led off in the direction of the field he owns on the opposite side of the lane, but unfortunately it was broken up during the work. What happened to the crusher?

JH Rieuwerts states that the miners must have explored beneath the shale east of Mill Dam as early as the 1650s. Smithy Coe was certainly in existence prior to 1682 since an agreement was made between John Radcliffe the owner and the partners of the Old Edge Mine to unwater their mine through a swallow in Smithy Coe in exchange for one of their four meers. After this there seems to be little information about Smithy Coe until the 19th Century.

Ashton A. Shuttleworth's accounts show that by 1815 he was paid £4.3s.1d for his 4/24 shares: a very meagre amount compared with what he was currently earning from Watergrove Mine near Wardlow Mires. Smithy Coe seems to have been more important for its swallow, which other mine owners who had difficulty unwatering their mines clearly coveted. Several agreements are recorded with its neighbouring mines of Old Edge in 1683 and New Edge in 1697 to help their drainage.

In 1858 an agreement was made with the owners of Smithy Coe, Walker and Ash miners of Great Hucklow, by the Mill Dam Mining Company to work the levels of Smithy Coe Mine below 300 feet. The Mill Dam Mining Company was to pay

The site of the Smithy Coe Mine shaft – somewhere beneath the present school playing field

them 4/- for every load of ore obtained below 300 feet: a good arrangement for Walker, Ash and Co. considering 1000 tons of ore per annum was raised between 1868-1878. In the 1850s it was known that there was a swallow in the old workings of Smithy Coe Mine at about 300 feet deep east of the gin shaft: the same swallow which had earlier helped to drain Old Edge and New Edge Mines. The Mill Dam Mining Company therefore acquired the workings below 300 feet in the hope that they could solve their drainage problems by either continuing their levels eastwards to the east swallow or sinking the Smithy Coe shaft still lower to find another possible swallow. The mine was worked to a depth of 492 feet, but the work to reach the swallows was never carried out. Possibly the yield of 1000 loads of ore per annum from the veins below 300 feet between 1868 and 1878 may have persuaded the owners of the Mill Dam Mining Company in 1870 to consider installing a new pumping engine instead. Mill Dam Mine was eventually closed down in 1884 but it is unclear exactly when Smithy Coe Mine was closed, though probably it was also around the same time as Mill Dam. Interestingly it appears the modern Mill Dam Mine uses the same swallows for some of its drainage.

In 1859 a letter from John SA Shuttleworth records the names of the proprietors of the upper section of Smithy Coe Mine as John Frost, farmer: Hucklow; Francis Ash, George Walker, Benjamin Walker. The letter says: 'it would be desirable that we should work the lower part of Have At All Mine through Smithy Coe if we could obtain reasonable terms.' We do not know whether he was successful.

Old Edge Mine

Old Edge Mine is situated according to Nellie Kirkham on a large mound on the southern border of the wood (field 75) but it is very difficult today to find any indication of the mine. This is disappointing since it was such an important mine in the seventeenth century. At some time it seems to have been within the same title as Smithy Coe. The limestone at this point was covered by a significant depth of shale, making access to the vein below more difficult.

John Bagshawe of Hucklow Hall bought the

mine in 1676. Between 1683 and 1701 a total of 7410 loads of ore were raised plus 3102 loads from New Edge Mine which Benjamin Ashton owned after October 1697. The shafts were sunk and the ore gained with hand labour only; no engines were employed on the Edge at this time. JH Rieuwerts comments that the absence of a horse gin was remarkable given the depth worked. Moreover its sough had been driven at very great expense through the shale by 1683 in order to allow the vein to be worked and drained into Smithy Coe Swallow. The partners must have considered this a worthwhile investment especially since they had to pay a quarter of four meers for the right to drive the sough as well as meeting their expenses. Apparently the vein could not be worked 'without liberty of a Watergate'.

In 1697 Mr Bagshawe also made an agreement with Benjamin Ashton to unwater New Edge Mine through the sough.

In 1730 the water mark for the mine is recorded as 486 feet. Between this date and the early 1800s little is known about the mine's output but the owners must have thought that the mine still had value since in 1836 they were involved in a dispute about the extent of their title.

The mine is now known to be situated on Sun vein, that is on the south side of the vein, but there seems to have been some confusion as late as 1836 about which mine was on which vein. This is quite understandable since the veins did not run in straight lines but split between riders into many branches. As can be seen from the map (p85) the vein known as Hucklow Edge Vein divides into Old Vein to the north east, on which Smithy Coe is situated, and Sun Vein to the east, where Old Edge shaft lay. Both veins join what is known as North Vein, on which New Edge Mine can be found.

Nellie Kirkham suggests that when Old Edge Shaft was first driven the miners assumed it was on Old Vein and not Sun Vein. This could well have led to confusion over different titles. Hence the dispute in 1836 when the Barmaster Mr Matthew Frost writes in a letter to Mr Wyatt:

'the purport of this is to inform you that I shall attend at Old Edge and New Edge mines on Wednesday 1st June next at 11 o'clock with four of the Grand Jury of the Kingsfield for the purpose of inquiry into and ascertaining the extent of the Old and New Edge title as there is a dispute how far such title extends eastwardly'.

New Edge Mine

New Edge Mine, situated in the wood just to the south of the Holloway, is easier to find. There is a very short mine road from the Holloway distinguished by two gate posts and modern railings which lead to foundations (barely discernable) of the mine buildings. The New Edge gin shaft is 700 feet south east of the school. The shaft was 482 feet deep and the total depth of workings was 492 feet. The shale ran to a depth of 300 feet so no ore could be found until the limestone was reached. In 1958 Nellie Kirkham drew plans of the mine as she found it but it is much more difficult to distinguish any of the remains today.

The earliest known record for the mine is a copy of an agreement among the Shuttleworth papers dated 1697 between John Bagshawe of Hucklow Hall and Benjamin Ashton of Stoney Middleton Hall, who had acquired the mine in October 1697. According to the document

'Mr Bagshawe's Groves (Old Edge mine) were adjoining the west end of the said meers of ground which are now in possession of the said Benjamin Ashton. Mr Ashton's meers were over burdened with water and also want a shaft and gates to work', so an agreement was signed to 'drive up a water gate or gates at their own charges and to drain and lay dry the said meers . . . and also to give free liberty to the said Benjamin Ashton and partners to carry their deads and boose and rubbish . . . through the gates belonging to Bagshawe's Edge Groves.'

This is an early example of the problems encountered in draining (unwatering) mines of such depth and an unusual cooperation considering the later disputes between the mines to the west of the Hucklow Liberty.

A further agreement of 1707 between Benjamin Ashton, now of Hathersage Hall, and William Bagshawe confirms this arrangement and states that

'Mr Ashton have been at great charges in endeavouring to get down a shaft but being overburdened with water cannot get down their shaft without the assistance and privilege of entering into the Old Edge Grove.'

It gives permission to him to drive a drift within the Old Edge ground and reciprocal arrangements were made for each party to use the other's ground for laying deads or rubbish 'to the least hindrance to the said groves'.

Whatever the water problems encountered in the lower levels, from 1697 to 1701 New Edge Mine produced 3,100 loads of ore and both Old Edge and New edge were moderately successful until 1711. However, by 1714 the combined output was only 145 loads.

Judging from a letter written in 1827 the mine could not have been worked for some time. A miner, Mr Oldfield threatened to nick it along with Old Edge and Have At All Mines and to have the title transferred to him.

Later, in 1836, it seems that the Shuttleworth family of Hathersage, descendants of the Ashtons, still had the title to the mine because the guardian of John Spencer Ashton Shuttleworth, an infant, paid the partners 7/24 and 1/96 interest as he understands the partners of Old and New Edge Mine are 'commencing workmanship' at these two mines. So it appears that Mr Oldfield did not have the title transferred to him and his threat of nicking the mines may have helped to restart work. It is also in 1836 that the Barmaster, Matthew Frost, sent the letter to Mr Wyatt about the dispute over the extent of the titles of Old and New Edge mines. It would be interesting to know what had provoked the letter.

Mr William Wyatt of Foolow occurs quite frequently as a busy mine agent who initially appears to have been very successful, appointed by the age of 21 as agent to several mines (1825) but latterly losing money. As a cousin of the Bagshaws he was agent for several mines on the Hucklow and Eyam Edges and later at High Rake Mine.

New Edge Mine appears to have been relatively successful in 1872 when we know 165 tonnes of lead ore was extracted. Presumably it did not have the drainage problems that Mill Dam Mine was suffering. After 1872, however, there was a rapid decline; 35 tonnes were extracted in 1877, 39 tonnes in 1878, and 16 tonnes in 1882. Comparatively, this must have been one of the more successful mines for John SA Shuttleworth.

Was this the end of the mine? Probably it was no longer financially viable since the price and demand for lead ore had dropped so considerably

Gate stoops on the access road to New Edge Mine from the Hollow Way

Site of the New Edge Mine Shaft

with cheaper imports from as far away as Spain and Australia. Even so, there is an entry in Kelly's Directory of 1891:

'Great Hucklow: New Edge Mine, Proprietor John Spencer Ashton Shuttleworth.'

Whether this suggests that even then someone was still working the mine, or merely indicates that the Shuttleworth family still owned the mineral rights and the hillocks is unclear. The hillocks were becoming valuable for their discarded minerals and the reference in the Wirksworth Parish registers 1896 to the New Edge Mining Co. producing lead ore, calc spar and sand seems to confirm this.

There is much debate about the drainage for Old Edge and New Edge Mines. JH Rieuwerts currently thinks that they must have been drained through a sough from Smithy Coe Mine towards Synings Lane and Little Hucklow. Previously, both

he and Nellie Kirkham thought that they must have been drained through Duce Hole swallow in Grindlow.

Gorse Bush Mine

There is some discrepancy in accounts as to the exact position of Gorse Bush Mine. It seems that documents from 1695 – 1700 refer to a mine close to Have At All Mine just south of the Holloway as it joins Abney road. The Hucklow Edge Vein divides into North vein, and South or Sun vein and further west into Old Vein not far from Gorse Bush mine. The miners were surprisingly good surveyors. They relied on a miner's dial, whose face was divided into 24 compass points made of brass and moulded on a well seasoned oak joist exactly one foot in length. Its accuracy was limited to around 2 degrees. They also had a sighting level, plumb bob and quadrant and a measuring chain.

Back o' the Edge or Ritheing Lake Mine

The name of this mine is worthy of a Nineteenth century Gothic novel. However, the real story of Back o' th' Edge or Ritheing Lake Mine is that of a frustrated race to exploit what was thought to be a promising lead vein running north west from a break in the Hucklow Edge vein at Old Grove Mine towards Camphill and the head of Bretton Clough.

William Bagshawe and partners wanted to explore this vein but were frustrated because the line of the vein went through the private liberty of Grindlow which at the time came under the Lordship of Viscount Cullen, who refused to allow Bagshawe a passage through. Bagshawe accordingly decided to sink a trial shaft at the head of Bretton Clough which was in the Hucklow liberty where the right of free search obtained since it was under the King's Lordship. He hoped to connect from there with the vein coming from Old Grove Mine in the Grindlow Liberty which shows how confident miners were in their surveying technique bearing in mind how much money was at risk. Beginning in 1759 he spent £288 from April to November – a considerable sum in those days – digging through a very deep series of shale beds. By December at least 17 men, some from Castleton, were employed.

Meanwhile in 1760-65 a rival consortium headed by Mr Clay from Bridgehouses, Sheffield, was driving through the shale a sough up from near Netherwater Farm in Stanlow Dale towards the same vein. Known as May Sough, it was a notable engineering achievement: the whole length would

have been about 3200 feet. In addition to this, a stretch of 1700 feet had probably already been driven in the 1750s. It seems that the knowledge of what Bagshawe and partners were up to motivated Clay into 'driving night and day'.

Events at the mine did not go well and the Bagshawe papers tell the tale; in April 1760 George Heywood mine agents said in a letter:

> 'Ritheing Lake Sough Engine Shaft hath been a very wet one as ever I saw down to the levill ...' and again 'this mine we think ought to be given up, we believe we have a vein under us that it is so overloaded with water that we think it can never be of service to us. Mr Bagshawe is minded to keep it in possession I suppose to see if anything can be discovered when Stoke Sough lets off water in the west of Edge Mine'.

The fate of so many miners on the Hucklow Edge really rested on this sough.

Little came of Back o' the' Edge Mine and in spite of much field-work by Nellie Kirkham and Doug Nash few remains of it were discovered on the surface. In 1976 Mr E Waller of Calver Edge Cottage, Eyam in conversation with Doug Nash declared, 'Back o' th' Edge Mine – I would not go into it even if there was a way' and added that Ned Maltby had told him when he was a boy 'all timber – like a coal mine, much water – very unsafe'. In 1953 Mr Joe Hancock, a member of the Windmill Barmote Jury, told Nellie Kirkham that until he was grown up he always knew Camphill Farm as Back o' th' Edge Farm.

In 1766 May Sough was recorded in the Hazelbadge liberty. In 1785 it was being worked

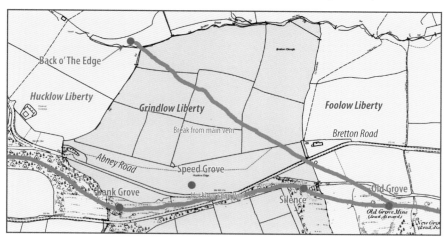

Map showing presumed site of Back o' Edge shaft which Bagshawe sank in the Hucklow Liberty as close as possible to the Grindlow Liberty border and in line with the vein which breaks NW from the main Hucklow Vein at Old Grove mine.

in the Hucklow liberty. Then the trail goes cold. No one it seems could have found the vein a successful investment but if the soughers did locate the vein it would be a tribute to their grit and determination.

The area currently known as the Washing Plant below the land slip from Camphill Edge is reputed to be the site of May Sough Mine. When Nellie Kirkham first visited in 1958 she found what she thought was a deserted dressing floor and 'Heath Robinson' apparatus, but in subsequent visits this

had disappeared. May Sough Mine is mentioned in the Bagshawe collection in 1762, 'delivered possession to Thos Bowman, Charlie Townend and Ann his wife'. Certainly there is a plentiful supply of water and the area was used as a washing plant earlier this century for minerals extracted from the hillocks. Judging from the profusion of mountain pansies which are lead tolerant (metallophytes) growing there in the spring the amount of lead pollution is likely to have been considerable.

The mines east of Mill Dam: 1700-2009
a pattern of revival and decline

After so much output in the early 1700s from the mines east of Mill Dam there is a dearth of information from about 1730-1820. We know the price for lead was low and many of the accessible veins exhausted. Once the mines reached a certain depth, drainage of the water became such a problem that until the horse-powered lifting gear could be replaced with efficient steam powered engines the mines probably became an unprofitable investment.

As at Back O' The Edge the owners may have held on to their titles in the hope that Stoke Sough might yet be the answer to their problems. Meanwhile perhaps the mines were only worked from time to time for small amounts of ore and investors turned their attention to more profitable mines. Moreover there was strong competition from the lead mines of the northern Pennines and by the late 1800s from cheap imports from Spain and Australia.

There was a revival of interest in the mines in the mid 1800s and new technology became available, but it needed considerable investment.

The only evidence we have found to date for the use of expensive steam powered engines in this area is for the Mill Dam Mining Co., The Great Hucklow Mining Co., namely Hill

top and Beech Grove mines and Silence mine in the Grindlow Liberty, none of which in the long run produced great returns for their investors. However, by the 1900s there was an increasing demand for the minerals discarded by the miner such as fluorspar and barytes and from then on there was a flourishing trade in reworking the hillocks. Even today these minerals are being sought beneath our feet in the Modern Mill Dam Mine.

Early 20th Century photograph of the old Edge Road in Hucklow Wood

9. The Grindlow Liberty

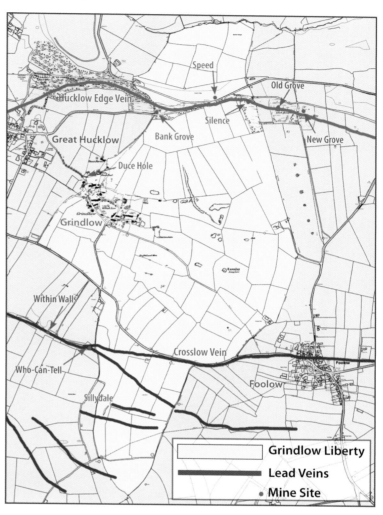

Grindlow has always been 'peculiar' in the sense of having a special status as a lead mining Liberty, the result of a series of historical events described later in this section. Apart from the significant mines on that section of Hucklow Edge Vein which passes through the north of the Liberty there is not much more to describe. There was a reasonably successful mining venture known as 'Within Walls' to the south of the village and also some discoveries of rich outcrops which didn't entail mining to any great depth.

In the mid 18thC Benjamin Bagshawe gives the following lead mining related description of Grindlow:

'The great Hucklow Edge Vein runs through Grindlow, the Speed and Silence are sunk on this vein. It was discovered first at Hucklow and on Tideslow, it is supposed to have been discovered about the year 1605 by judging of the coins that have been found at Hucklow.

Old William Bagshawe says that there was the best work in the croft behind Ralph's House near the pool he ever saw, he drove the engine at that mine. In the same vein about 100 yards below it (East) there is a shackhole with a little shaft in the bottom of it but filled. About 200 yards still east there is a shaft sunk plumb on the vein, the vein is nearly five feet wide, the shaft is about 20 fathoms from the surface in the same vein east in Grindlow fields. Old James Frost had a very good mine but the ground was so heavy that it all run-in, you may see shaft filled to the top on the line of the vein, the hillocks were lead away when the ground was improved by Benjamin Wyatt, my uncle.

William (the farmer) worked at a small shaft that they sunk on the north side of the lane near an old building called Halls Old House, they drew all the stuff up by a rope and an old can, they got a fother of lead out of it. The vein faded and soon the ore went out in a spar leader at the bottom of the shaft, and they being young did not care to sink being tired of mining. They took their rubbish to Douse Hole and dropped it there. I think it was connected with a pipe there.

Is one somewhere near that place, the top of Jagger House Lane and just at the stile that goes from there to Hucklow on foot road, the miners that worked there last left a rib of lead ore the thickness of four inches but something happening they ran away. The mineral is very rich here yellow and Cauky there is a scrin runs through my grandfather's garden.

On the top of the Well Yart there is a range of hillocks, same vein as behind Ralph's, at the intersection of the vein and the footroad there is a great quantity of ore the old men say, it is at no depth. Before the houses under Chapel they find ore anywhere near it and I think that is the pipe. The old men say that there is a shaft bound over, in the little croft fair south from Douse Hole, a very rough piece, there is some nice bowse left by the old man ready got and also some old man's tools.

There is a day level drove up to Have At All from the Douse. My Uncle William found leaders of ore whilst making garden near the top of the Knowle with blowing the rock up. I should think that these would be pipe leaders there being no vein with in 50 or 60 yards.

About 200 yards from Jagger House Lane there is a vein which has never been much cut, it run-in and some men spreading manure for Mr Wyatt found the run. I looked, it was only a yard deep but there was first rate stuff in it, you may see it at the extreme corner of the Grindlow Manor at the junction of the Jagger House Lane and the Tideswell Road and also on the north corner of the Within Wall in Great Hucklow Liberty. A little more west one field from the Within Wall in a small field now in the possession of Henry Dakin there was a small mine worked not so long since and they had a rib of ore as thick as a mans thigh, my uncle Sam of Grindlow can remember it worked.'

This account seems typical of the free miners gaining what lead they could on a fairly small scale while maintaining their farms. The mines on the Hucklow Edge were organised, worked and developed on a much larger scale.

One significant feature on the edge of the village is 'Douse Hole' mentioned above. This is a swallet and takes much of the water draining down from the land above. In his walk around the Liberty Doug Nash notes:

'The party made its way through Grindlow village and paused at Duce Hole and the swallow there. The swallow is currently being excavated by the Stockport Caving Club and good progress is being made. It is of interest that a dye test made from here some years ago showed up, according to report, in Bagshawe Cavern, Bradwell. This suggests a turning point in the underground drainage, since points east of here all appear to drain towards Waterfall Swallet to the south-east, this swallow must run north-west to get to Bradwell.'

Part of the Duce or Douse Swallet. The 'Douse Hole' is hidden by the trees to the top-right of the photograph.

A 'Customary Lordship'

The Grindlow Liberty became a Customary Lordship, (ie one that operated outside of the Kingsfield)) as a result of a particular sequence of historical events, and we are grateful to Andrew Bower for researching much of the detail in the following section.

In the late 12 Century, Matthew, son of Walltheof of Stoke, granted Grindlow to Lilleshall Abbey in Shropshire. This grant was confirmed by King John on 31st August 1199 and so Grindlow ceased to be controlled by the Crown. At various times the grant was reaffirmed by Matthew's descendants but of particular significance is a confirmation c1198 which mentions 'All the land at Grindlow and all mining rights within the bounds of the said land'. In a further confirmation by Aricia of Stoke (c1220-27) it is noted that the Canons ' may sell, mortgage or let at farm the aforesaid lands with all appurtences in any way they wish'.

The boundaries of Grindlow Grange, as it became known, are described in an entry in the Lilleshall Charters written in the 14th Century (a Grange is a parcel of buildings and land owned by a religious House or Order, like Abney Grange just over the hill to the north). Neither the Augustinian Canons nor their Lay Brothers were actively engaged in mining activities, but could let (farm) the mining rights as they wished. Following the ravages of the Black Death the income of the abbey declined rapidly, and it was usual from the mid 14th Century for such abbeys to rent out their granges.

The land was not particularly productive from an agricultural point of view because in 1318 the abbey decided to sell off a messuage and 13 acres adjacent to the grange since the land was 'more burdensome than fruitful' due to the various charges imposed by the bailiffs of Peveril Castle. In c1358 the grange was occupied by a solitary canon and a shepherd.

Immediately prior to the dissolution of the monasteries Grindlow Grange was in the hands of the Bradshawe family who let it to four tenants mostly engaged in sheep rearing but who

'. . . dowe pay yearlye to the churche of lichfeld xxˢ
for all mano(rial) tythes to mynye and growings of
the grange . . .'

At the dissolution of Lilleshall Abbey in 1538 the inventory of its assets included 'leade remaynyng unsolde . . . 100 fothers at £4 the fother . . . £400'. Compared to this sum the entire contents of the abbey seem a little paltry as they were valued at £74.18s (except for its bells, some church plate and various pavings) and the annual income of the abbey from all its holdings came to around £340 per annum.

The dissolution of Lilleshall was the responsibility of William Cavendish and Thomas Legh who efficiently returned the holdings of the abbey to the Exchequer. William became the second husband of Bess of Hardwick in 1547, the same year that Edward VI came to the throne. William and Bess purchased Chatsworth and Edensor in 1549, and in 1552 William gave all his property and lands in other counties to the Crown in exchange for a massive tranche of lands, most of which were in Derbyshire. Grindlow was part of this exchange and William is likely to have recognised its value as a potential source of lead for the new house at Chatsworth. A hundred-year ownership of Grindlow by the Cavendish family had begun.

Unfortunately for them the Cavendish family chose the wrong side in the Civil War and their estates were subsequently compounded by the Commonwealth. While they eventually regained much of their land the manor of Grindlow and its attendant rights was eventually bought by Sir John Harpur (of Swarkstone, Breadsall and Caulke) following the Restoration. Sir John married Francis, daughter of Lord Willoughby. When her husband died Frances married the Earl of Bellamont, taking the Grindlow Manor rights with her. The mines had 'accustomary inheritance . . . from ancestor to heir', and wives were dowerable.

Thus Grindlow became one of the several lead mining 'Liberties' which could operate independently of the 'Kingsfield' by which it was surrounded. It was also a 'Customary Lordship' in which a grant had been made by the Crown of the minerals as well as the land, and therefore held customary privileges of Derbyshire lead mining. In this Lordship

'any of the King's liege subjects of the realm . . . . .
may become Mynors of the Liberty of Grindlow

.... may dig or search for mines or veins of lead ore wherever they could be found, except under a church, church yard, house or garden, or highway .... and take up and posses any new or old Veins, Rake or Mine by setting of Stoces made and pind with wood .... openly on the surface'

and they could work the mines according to custom. The laws for the manor were stated in the Great Barmote Court for the Liberty of Grindlow in 1713 and were by and large much the same in principal to all the other Liberties of the Derbyshire orefield (see 'Laws and Customs' section p16).

Lady Bellamont granted the Benjamin Ashton partnership the right of Barmastership, the Lord's meer, and the freeing dish for the founder meers, and lot and cope, so that they were what was known as the 'farmers' of the mineral duties in the Liberty for twenty-one years at £140 a year. This business deal was probably a very 'hard-nosed' bargain as the Liberty was not worth much until the mineral vein under Hucklow Edge began to be exploited.

The deal also meant that anyone wanting to mine in Grindlow had to be given the title to do so by the Barmaster appointed by the partners.

The title to a mine or vein, and the fact the partners were now also Lords of the Field, were two separate things – in view of the subsequent trouble, as described later in this section, the point is important. In the case of Bank, Speed and Silence Mines, the partners combined the possession of both Title and Lordship. Thus the partners could apply for title to their own Barmaster, and would be granted title by him, and could retain the title so long as they kept their possession stowes in proper order, and continued to work the mines. This was also important for if it could be shown that a mine had not been worked for three weeks then it could be 'arrested' and the title taken by someone else. The title was perpetual as long as they fulfilled these conditions and the twenty-one years' lease in a customary liberty applied to the farming out of the duties.

This was a situation which lead eventually to a series of events known as the 'Grindlow Riots', mainly because they occasioned the reading of The Riot Act. In spite of being associated with this brief period of turbulence, Grindlow was a peaceful and typical lead mining community, as Andrew Bower shows in the following piece about the social history of the village.

Grindlow – some aspects of its Social and Industrial History
by Andrew Bower

Names of Grindlow residents can be compiled from the 16th Century but it is not until the census returns of the 19th Century that there is detailed information on the inhabitants and their occupations. Prior to 1841 information must be sought from documents held in public and private collections and of these the Bagshawe Collection in Sheffield Archives is of particular interest. The collection is that of E. G. Bagshawe (died 1956) and his father Benjamin (died 1907), both of whom were solicitors with keen antiquarian interests. E. G. Bagshawe's grandfather was also called Benjamin and was born in Grindlow in 1807 to John Bagshaw and Margaret (the daughter of William Wyatt of Foolow). Benjamin senior was executor to the will of his cousin (also named William Wyatt) who was a solicitor and mineral agent.

As solicitors, antiquarians and local landowners the Bagshawes had an understandable interest in documents relating to land ownership, mining rights and customs in this area. Genealogical notes were compiled to clarify details of inheritance. After E. G. Bagshawe died the vast collection of papers and documents were entrusted to Sheffield Archives. One particularly helpful item is the Overseers of the Poor Account book 1803-1861.

Before the Poor Law Amendment Act of 1834 the local Overseers were empowered to raise funds for distribution to the poor of their parish or township. Their duties seem to extend to include various local administrative tasks regarding felonies, census returns, highway maintenance and so on. After 1834 parishes were combined into unions which took over much of the responsibility for the poor of the area. The Bakewell Poor Law

Union came into being in 1838 and rented a private workhouse in Ashover until the Bakewell Workhouse was completed at Newholme in 1841. The overseers' accounts tell us some of the names of the wealthier residents who provided funds and of the impoverished in need of their support. The Amendment Act did not completely end local care and the overseers' accounts continue to detail some distributions to those in need.

Other documents providing social history material include directories, wills, deeds, gravestone inscriptions and personal letters, some of which now turn up on the Internet.

Landholding

Over the centuries the residents of Grindlow have paid rent to a succession of gentry landowners: the Cavendish family from 1552 until the mid 17th Century; the Harpur family of Swarkestone; and then the Cokayne family (Lords Cullen of Rushton, Northants) throughout the 18th Century and into the Nineteenth. With the extinction of the Cullen baronacy the estate passed via the Cokayne daughters and the Cox family into the hands of Andrew Brittlebank of Winster. After his death, his third wife Catherine (née Catherine Margaretha Korn) mortgaged part of her inheritance but then redeemed the mortgage and decided to sell off her freeholds in Grindlow Township. The sale of 1878 allowed some locals to buy outright houses that their families had been tenants of for generations. The sale also allowed some incomers the chance to buy anew. Silence Mine was still in production at this time and the sale particulars note that the mineral rights under the Hucklow Edge area within Grindlow are leased to 'Messrs Carreer and others' until March 25th 1897. No interest is shown in any mineral right within the hamlet of Grindlow whereas the value of timber on each plot is specified. Back in the 17th Century when William Cavendish drew up deeds for his tenants he was quite clear about reserving the mineral rights under each and every property.

Samuel Bagshaw's Directory of 1846 states that Grindlow has 30 houses in 1789, a number which reduced to 24 by 1811. White's Directory of 1857 records a population of 101 in 1801 rising to 119 in 1821 and falling to 87 in 1831. The first detailed census return in 1841 shows that a population of 110 lived in 20 households. From then on there was a gradual decline so that by 1901 there were 31 residents in only 9 inhabited dwellings.

As of December 2007 there are 13 households in Grindlow proper and 3 outlying dwellings. It should be noted that 2 houses apparently in Grindlow actually fall within Great Hucklow: these are Duce Farm and 'Green Acres'.

Where are the missing houses? Some cottages of landless miners as well as larger dwellings have disappeared with little or no trace. The buildings of Grindlow are invariably built on solid bedrock and when demolished leave no evidence of foundations, the materials when reused leave only fragments of dressed stone to inform the keen eye. The number of households within each building could easily change, farmhouses being divided into several cottages and often back again.

Water

On limestone ground this essential resource soon disappears and various ways had to be found to contain it. Benjamin Bagshawe writing c. 1869 with regard to an interruption to the supply to Great Hucklow troughs noted there was 'no other water to be had except for the adjoining manor of Grindlow . . . the water supply there is very limited in dry weather.'

Water for human consumption was obtained from a well to the north of Rose Farm which is clearly marked on early O.S. maps. Another well is marked in fields to the north of Hall Farm. Individual households would contrive their own methods of catchment. Large gritstone troughs could collect water from downpipes and at Lane Head Farm roof run-off was directed into a large underground tank.

Grindlow had two large pools of water named Duce Pool and Bagshaw Pool. The latter provided cattle watering to all local residents via a now incomplete lane immediately to the east of Grind Low (the 'low' being the small knoll in the centre of the hamlet). Bagshaw Pool is not named as such but is clearly shown on William Senior's map of 1631. It no longer exists but a low-lying area flanked by ancient hawthorns marks its position.

Duce Pool lay on the northern township boundary with Great Hucklow and collected water that drained down from Hucklow Edge.

The Overseers Accounts note the emptying of 'Dows Pool' in the autumn of 1809, and in the spring of 1821 15s was spent on cleaning 'Dows Pool'. Since public funds were being spent it is likely that this pool was a communal resource.

Population and Occupations

With lead mining providing work for many locals the price of lead had a direct impact on the viability of the mines and the wellbeing of the community. The productive years of the early 18th Century would have provided welcome income whilst the Grindlow dispute of the mid 18th Century must have driven the local miners elsewhere in search of a wage. As lead prices fluctuated then plummeted in the late 18th Century hardship set in. William Wyatt of Foolow writing in 1796 noted that

> '... the poor people in this neighbourhood never suffer'd as they do now' and four years later, "This part of the country is sore distressed for Bread, how shall we manage until the next Crop I do not know". His diary states, "A strange Xmas this. I have known every family in this Town have plenty of roast beef pies, Cheese and Ale etc ... At this time there is not more than five families here that has bread enough."

In 1790 the Grindlow Overseers of the Poor, when asked to provide 'a place of reception for Paupers and Vagrants', were able to claim 'We have no Pauper to inhabit ye same'. It was accepted that the village constable, Robert How, would provide a room in his house to fulfil the county's requirement. In 1801 the Overseers accounts tell a different story with several individuals receiving weekly payments as well as extra assistance e.g. to Mary How for 'two shifts 6s 6d, pair of shoes 6s 6d'. Throughout the early 19th Century the overseers helped with clothing, shoe mending, rent arrears and household repairs as well as doctor's fees and, inevitably, coffins for all ages. Lead prices more than doubled between March 1799 and March 1806 which improved the miners' situation but it seems the legacy of a larger 18th Century population was a sizeable number of widows.

From 1841 the census returns show names and occupations: out of 110 people, 13 were lead miners, 8 were farmers, 1 a lead smelter and 2 were cotton weavers. Greater detail in 1851 indicates that 10 of the 17 households engaged in farming a total of 237 acres, 18 people were lead miners whilst 2 farmers also mined: Rachael Bamford was a handloom weaver and her elderly aunt Martha a bobbin winder. By 1861, 7 of the 14 households were working farms and 13 males (7 of which were no older than 14) were lead miners. John Frost was a farmer of 27 acres and a lead mine proprietor whilst William Bagshaw farmed only 9 acres but was also a lead smelter. One William Pickford aged 21 was a lead miner with a wife Mary and 8 month old son Robert, by 1871 he had moved to Bretton with 3 more children all born in Grindlow.

In 1871 only 6 men are recorded as miners whilst 4 were lead ore dressers. Only 144 acres were farmed by 6 households and the population had dropped to 53. By 1881 there were only 5 miners and by 1891 there were none. Agriculture remained the principal occupation.

During the 19th Century other occupations appear in the Overseer's Accounts and the census returns. Textile working could be carried out in the home by women and those unable to farm or mine. The Overseers record payments related to textile working for instance in June 1808 Mary How received 'a pair of wool cards ... 3s 6d'. In July 1816 William Bagshaw is given 6s to pay 'loom rent' whilst in 1829 2s is spent 'setting Jack on weaving a shuttle' and a further 10s 8½d was spent on his weaving equipment.

The census returns note labourers, farm servants, dairy maids, butter dealers and a boot maker. Thomas Hancock is a farmer and oil merchant in 1891 and by 1901 his sons Moses and Aaron (their mother Ellen was sister to twins Moses and Aaron) work with him as licensed Hawkers. Aaron is mentioned elsewhere as a high achiever at Great Hucklow School. He went on to found a chain of grocery stores with a branch in Tideswell and others throughout the district.

Grindlow produced other high achievers in earlier centuries. In the mid 17th Century 'Francis Bennit in Grinlo' was able to produce his own coinage in the form of a token which depicted a lead miner's pick. In 1684 'ffrancis James of Grinlow in the county of Derby miner' was able to lease 'all... Sr Daniel Fleming's lead-mines on ye North side of ye river which runneth by Coniston forge in ye County of Lancaster'.

Grindlow from Hucklow Edge

In the 18th Century Richard White of Grindlow was a lead merchant who amassed mine holdings which were inherited by his son Richard of Tideswell in 1772 and by his grandson Samuel in 1803. When Samuel died in 1810 his property and portfolio of mine shares was auctioned at the Old George Inn, Tideswell. Included in the sale was '… a very commodious cupola for the smelting of lead situate in the liberty of Eyam'. This was the Bretton Cupola to which one imagines much local ore must have been sent by the White family. Richard White Senior and his son are buried in the family grave at Eyam parish church. The simple grandeur of the grave slab and its particular location (adjacent to Catherine Mompesson) bear testament to the Whites' position in society.

Finally the generation of Bagshaws that grew up in Hall Farm, Grindlow, in the early years of the 19th Century produced not only Benjamin, but also Samuel who produced his 'History Gazetteer and directory of Derbyshire' in 1846, followed by similar volumes for Kent (1847), Cheshire (1850) and Shropshire (1854). The youngest brother Henry became the owner of a steelworks in Sheffield.

One particular character named Charles Frost serves to illustrate several fascinating aspects of 19th Century life. Charles was a lead miner and lay preacher who lived with his elderly mother Elizabeth and held prayer meetings at home. On Monday, November 13th, 1815, he had the misfortune to be caught in a rockfall whilst alone in an 'old work' 120 feet below the surface. His legs were trapped but, in total darkness, he freed himself to find one leg badly broken. Despite his dire situation he raised his spirits with song and prayer until Thursday evening when miners from surrounding villages located him. On reaching the surface he was greeted by his future wife Mary Baggaley then carried home on a sofa and a doctor summoned. At first things went badly as the hot water bottles and hot bricks prescribed caused his legs to 'mortify'. Amputation was recommended but a second opinion was sought and eventually Charles's legs healed as best they could. Mining was clearly out of the question as future employment and Charles is listed as a farmer in the census return from 1841 to 1861.

In 1841 his son Robert was a saw-making apprentice whilst his elder brother William was working on the farm. The sons left home by 1851 and headed for America. Robert wrote home in 1871 and included a picture of his residence in Winchester, Illinois. Eventually he became a banker and is recorded as having been in Scott County, Illinois for 30 years before his death in 1888.

Charles's wife Mary died in June 1861 so he decided to leave for America to join his sons. He travelled on Brunel's Great Eastern and the sticks he had needed since his accident helped him on the rolling deck of the ship when it encountered stormy weather. With hymns, faith and prayers he raised the morale of terrified fellow passengers until the ship arrived safely in New York. This must have occurred before 1864 when the Great Eastern was sold off to become the vessel that laid the first transatlantic cable.

Another Grindlow chap left home for totally different reasons. Robert Bagshaw, son of William the lead smelter, is listed as a lead miner aged 19 in 1851. Four years later he left for London where he signed up for the Army Works Corps. After a brief stay at the Ramblers Rest, Norwood and a visit to the *'Christall Palace'* he headed to the Crimea aboard the Ballackpore. Once at Ballaclava he was to help build a military railway to supply the siege of Sebastapol. This is only known because this good son wrote home to recount his experiences and wish family and friends well.

He sent regards to the *'Dusty Pit workmen'*, so perhaps he had worked in the Dusty Pit Mine to the north of the road from Foolow to Eyam.

Whilst Robert was away this mine enjoyed booming production and raised large quantities of first rate ore peaking at over 550 tons in the annual accounts of 1857.

Grindlow's strong agricultural base must have helped soften the effects of downturns in the lead market that hit hard amongst the landless communities.

The hamlet has changed remarkably little over the centuries compared to other villages where expansion and infilling obscure the original settlements. Although social conditions may be vastly different earlier generations would recognise the place but wonder where the lead miners had gone.

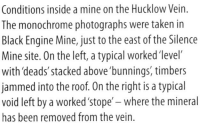

Conditions inside a mine on the Hucklow Vein. The monochrome photographs were taken in Black Engine Mine, just to the east of the Silence Mine site. On the left, a typical worked 'level' with 'deads' stacked above 'bunnings', timbers jammed into the roof. On the right is a typical void left by a worked 'stope' – where the mineral has been removed from the vein.

The colour photograph is of Moorwood Sough, built to drain the Eyam Edge mines. The roof is particularly remarkable – beatifully worked slabs of limestone locked at the apex by a 'key stone', and supporting a filling of 'deads'.

(photographs by Paul Deakin)

Grindlow Liberty Mines on the Hucklow Edge Vein

Bank Grove and Speed Grove Mines

Bank Grove and Speed Grove were in the Grindlow liberty. Bank could be the oldest Grindlow mine on the Hucklow Edge Vein although some records imply that Silence Mine was working by 1610. Bank was worked from 1712 and in 1713 produced 4,500 loads of ore from the mine and 2,300 loads of ore from the hillocks. The total ore sold between 1712 and 1714 was 8,000 loads of mined and 3,180 of hillock ore. From then on production declined until all accounts cease in 1733 and little is known about the mine after that date. Nellie Kirkham located Bank Grove south of the Abney Road to the west of Have it All mine. Here she detected walls of a small building in the hillside.

Speed Grove is situated just to the north of the present Abney Road not far from its junction with the Bretton Road. Nellie Kirkham did some field work to locate it in 1953 and '58 but she found only what seemed to be a shaft mound on the north edge of the road and slight remains of hillocks. It is possible that much of the remains of Speed Mine was destroyed by hillocking.

The production of ore began at Speed in 1713 and until 1722 the mine seems to have produced a moderate amount, but like Bank its reckonings cease by 1733 and it doesn't appear in the records again until 1757. The three mines Bank, Speed and Silence seem to have been in some form of Consolidated Title from 1740.

In 1746 Joseph Drabble, an overseer at Stoke Sough, gave evidence in a court case that the ore got from Speed Mine was by blasting which meant it was very hard to work.

Speed is principally interesting for the involvement of its miners in the Grindlow Riots in 1737 (recounted in the later section on Silence Mine p98) and the detailed reckonings for 16 July 1753 given in the Bagshawe Collection: *'of the ore extracted below the water mark.'* 'Plumbed and levelled Speed engine shaft, – gates (climbing shafts) *from surface at shaft top to the deepest soles* (bottom) *they then worked in the east end from the gate'*.

JH Rieuwerts thinks we cannot assume that this was in preparation for the actual opening of Stoke Sough even though according to the reckonings on the 2nd July 1757 Speed Mine appears to be paying 'composition' to Stoke Sough for the first time. (See note on Stoke Sough p107)

The last entry seen for cutting through the cranch (a particularly hard piece or section of rock) at Bradshaw Engine was 26 April 1757. This mine was situated in the Foolow Liberty further along the rake. However, Rieuwerts does not think this means that the drive through the cranch was complete and the water level had only then dropped at Speed Mine. There is no evidence that water was flowing eastwardly to Stoke Sough in the 1760s and it could be that the Stoke Soughers were also involved in work at Duce Hole in Grindlow to which Have At All mine was probably already draining. The problem with Duce Hole is that it provides very little scope for drainage. The water would have to be raised, or pumped so high before it could be discharged into the sough.

View from the site of Speed Mine

Pieces of mined minerals from the surviving spoil heaps at Speed Mine – shale, limestone and fluorspar

The description in the Bagshaw papers of the establishing of the water marks gives us a detailed account of the complex mine workings. The engine shaft was 350 feet deep and the level then went off eastwards via four different sumps (short shafts). A level also went westwards to a 10 feet sump into a dipping drift which descended into the water. The water marks were put in at 498 feet. These were necessary to mark the difference any future drainage might make and so to estimate the payment due to the sough master or pump engine proprietor for the agreed amount of ore mined below the mark.

Within the Bagshaw papers there is mention of a bill from Thos. Froggatt 1773 to Lady Day 1774 and then a reference to belland at Speed Grove in 1787, but after this we have no mention of the mine.

Silence Mine and the Grindlow Riots

Silence Mine was one of the more successful mining ventures along the Hucklow Vein in terms of the amount of ore produced and the return on capital invested from the sale of the ore. In a transcription of the proceedings for an action at the Kings Bench in the 1740s, it was stated in evidence by a William Mettam that: 'There was a flat in Silence (mine) 40 or 50 yards wide'. In mining parlance a 'flat' was a vein of mineralization lying between horizontal bedding planes as opposed to a vertical rake vein – which means that this had to be an extremely significant ore-bearing vein; such a mine having a vein of this magnitude would be regarded as very valuable. The name of the mine is said to derive from the miners' name for this vein – Silence Vein, although towards the end of its life it was also referred to as 'Chatty's Mine' (Kirkham).

Like many such ventures Silence Mine had a difficult beginning and its eventual demise came slowly as the lead became more difficult to win. It was one of the last mines on the Hucklow Vein to close.

The mines along this part of Hucklow Vein were originally served by the miners' way which would have been laid out by the Barmaster and two of the Grand Jury for the use of the miners, now known by a variety of names including Silence Lane, Blackberry Lane and even Rabbit Lane. Although it is a peaceful enough place now, it was not always so. Successful lead mining activities always ran the risk of dispute, argument and sometime violence, and Silence Mine had its share of all three. How fiercely the rights of miners were contested and how litigation by miners and owners became almost a way of life is illustrated by the happenings at Silence Mine and in the Liberty of Grindlow.

The site of the mine itself lies in a wooded area on the south side of Bretton Edge Road. The shale hillocks still surround the site of what would have been the working shaft.

Until the Peak District Mines Historical Society began excavating in 2008 not much could be seen of the original workings except the remnants of some stone buildings, one with a very well built arched roof. As the excavations have progressed more and more has been revealed and eventually much will be learned about the layout and working of the mine.

The area itself is part of the Silence Heritage Site, a beautiful setting of naturalised scrub and grassland which is managed by the two adjoining Parishes of Great Hucklow and Foolow as a nature reserve and heritage site.

Below the mine site is a sough or, more properly a shale gate, which carried pumped drainage water from the mine itself. The 'tail' of the sough was still visible in the 1960s where it emerged as a water pipe feeding a cattle trough in the field below the mine site. When it was an active sough it would have had a larger entrance and in the 1950s the farmer and a companion opened it between the tail and the bottom of the wood. They found the interior was only crawling height, the roof fashioned from flat shale, propped with larch poles every few feet. Water from the tail sinks into a slab-covered drain which goes southwards for about 1700ft to Piece End, and eventually into the stream which feeds Waterfall Swallet.

Initially it is likely that the drawing shaft of Silence Mine was served by a horse-gin and this may have been situated on the ground somewhere to the north of the shaft. There is evidence that the buildings above the shaft housed a later 'engine'. There is an extant sketch plan of the site in the

Derbyshire Records Office showing an engine and boiler house, a circular chimney, a capstan and a shaft with headstocks. Much of this is now coming to light. The coal bunkers have been revealed, confirming the use of a steam engine. Though it was a successful mine, water eventually became too much of a problem and it eventually closed down in the 1880s.

Records are vague as to how early mining began on the site. In 1713, Benjamin Ashton, *'Gentleman, of Hathersage'*, and his partners, made an indenture with the Countess of Bellamont who owned the manor of Grindlow, and therefore the mineral rights of the land on which Silence Mine is situated. By 'driving Trying and Sinking into ye Earth, at a great Hazard and very great Expense' the partners of the mine 'did find out and discover at a great depth' veins of lead ore. The 'great Hazard and very great Expense' was engendered because mining on this part of the Hucklow Edge Vein meant driving through a considerable depth of shale capping to the limestone beds and the mineral veins. No doubt these gentlemen thought the effort and expense would be worthwhile, but they had to be sure that their possession of the right to mine the site was secure enough to justify their considerable outlay.

The Silence Mine shaft was sunk 328 feet through the shale capping to reach the limestone bed beneath and eventually went into this a further 198 ft. It can be surmised that the sough mentioned above must have been a 'pumpway' with the drainage from the mine water being raised mechanically to the sough level.

The boundaries of the old lead mining Liberties of Grindlow and Eyam more or less follow the present parish/ward boundaries of Great Hucklow and Foolow. These ancient Liberties often had different and distinct practices and freedoms. Silence Mine and the neighbouring Bank Grove and Speed Mines were all on the Hucklow Edge Old Vein but lay within mineral liberty of Grindlow which operated as a separate entity from that of Great Hucklow within the 'Kingsfield'. Because the vein ran continuously through both Liberties arguments, lawsuits and eventually violence arose between the various interested parties of miners, mineral rights owners and lessees, mining partnerships, landowners and Barmasters.

The tail of Silence Sough where it emerges in the meadow below the Silence Heritage Site.

It is worth following these events in some detail in order to see how lead mining could be subject to complicated ancient rights and laws and fraught with pitfalls which could be even deeper than the mines themselves.

The Countess of Bellamont died in 1714 and left the manor of Grindlow to Charles Cokayne, Viscount Cullen, the son of her sister Catherine Willoughby, the property descending to her by inheritance. The lessee partners continued to pay the yearly rent of £140 to Cullen, or his agent. Benjamin Ashton died in 1725, and the mines continued to be worked by the other partners, among them being Aymer Rich, of Bullhouse, Yorkshire, who had married Grace Bagshawe of Great Hucklow Hall, and through her inherited the manor of Great Hucklow and also a share in the Grindlow mines.

During the latter part of the lease of the Lordship from Lady Bellamont they had worked the mines 'at great loss and expense . . . the levels and soles of the Groves having been greatly troubled with water', but by 1735 they had 'now a prospect of being very soon relieved of ye water taken or carried from ye sd three Groves or lead mines by means of a Sough or levell that is now bringing up' and which would 'in short time unwater and lay dry ye deepest soles'.

In the early 1730s, when Stoke Sough was being driven westwards from the River Derwent to drain the Eyam Edge Mines, water-marks were made in

The road known locally as Silence Lane, laid out by the Barmote Court to access the mines below Bretton Edge.

them, and an agreement was made that the watermarks for the mines in the Grindlow Liberty were to be 498 feet below the surface at Speed Mine, and 486 feet from here to Old Edge Mine in Hucklow.

Trouble began in 1737 when Viscount Cullen saw his chance to cash in on the hard work of the miners. It had become common knowledge that the Hucklow Edge vein was continuing rich below the water table, particularly should Stoke Sough come so far and drain the mine in depth. Cullen insisted that the 21 year lease (1713 – 1734) applied to the mine and the mineral rights, and he tried to take it over.

As was typical elsewhere, the large gentry-owned mines operated alongside small free mining operations, worked by the miners when they were not at labour in the deep mines. Cullen's claim upon the mining rights therefore prejudiced both the title of the investors and the miners' livelihood as copers (miners who worked on a 'bargain' basis for a mine owner) and free miners (miners who worked solely on their own account). Most lead mining disputes tended to oppose the miners and the mine owners. Here the alignment of opposing interests in Grindlow pushed the miners

into alliance with the mine-owners against the freeholders and holders of mining rights.

The mine-owners started legal action against Cullen at the Derby Assizes in 1737, who passed the matter on to the Court of Common Pleas in 1738. In July 1738, the Common Pleas ruled in favour of Lord Cullen's possession of the mineral rights of Grindlow. This judgement was both preceded and followed by a series of increasingly violent confrontations which formed the basis of further action by Lord Cullen at the Court of King's Bench in 1739. The narrative of events which emerges from the legal papers of the King's Bench case deserves recounting, pointing as it does to the potential willingness of the eighteenth-century miners to resort to strenuous action in defence of their rights.

In March 1738, Lord Cullen's agent, Warren, raised the freeholders of Grindlow in an attack upon the miners, after which he took forcible possession of the mines. In an act of deliberate provocation, Warren burnt the stowes which marked possession of the mine. A threatening crowd of miners gathered, and Warren's men left off. Early in June, Warren again attempted to take the mines, but was driven off by crowds of miners. On 10 July 1738, in defiance of the Court of Common Pleas verdict, the deep mines were formally reopened by the mine-owners. Two days later, officers of the county's Sheriff arrived to enforce the law. The deputy Sheriff gave an account of the events of that day. When he and forty of his men came to the mine:

'there was a very great number of people . . . two hundred or more about the said mine called Bank (Grove) many of them swore that they valued no writts or power And that if the Sheriff or any man took possession of the said mines they would have his blood.'

The crowd, made up of both men and women, threw stones at the Sheriff's officers. Despite the reading of the Riot Act again one of the Sheriff's men was attacked by members of the crowd, at which point 'a bloody battle ensued', as others turned on the deputy Sheriff crying, 'Damm him kill that Blue Coat Dog . . . he's Warren's man'.

The officers of the law were driven off by this little insurrection, following which the miners blockaded the entrances to the mines. An armed guard of thirty or forty men was mounted upon the mines, maintaining their watch in eight-hour shifts, and word given out that 'the partners would raise all the miners in the High Peak and take possession of the said mines back again'.

Rumours circulated that Warren would attempt to retrieve possession by force, that he would bring soldiers for that purpose 'and that in case any resistance was made he would murther or destroy them all'.

Finally, on 22 July the Sheriff's men approached the mine again. 'They heard . . . people on the said mines give several great shouts . . . and also beat a drum upon the mines', which the Sheriff's men 'took to be a signal to call in people to their assistance'. A crowd of allegedly armed and drunken miners, 'picked and chosen from other mines and other places in the County as a set of daring and desperate fellows fittest to undertake any wild enterprise', rallied support. A crowd of 200 people assembled from the neighbouring villages, many also armed; 'Several of the rioters [swore] . . . that no possession should be taken and that they would lose their lives before.'

The Riot Act was again read by the Sheriff, but to no effect. According to the miners, the Sheriff's men attacked them, but they held back, crying to one another, 'good lads, hold your hands, pray don't strike'. By the evening, the crowd had grown to 500 people, again comprising both men and women. The Sheriff sensibly recoiled from confronting such a large crowd and retired.

In the two riots of July 1738, Cullen's opponents had succeeded in driving off the Sheriff and his officers. But advice from the mine-owners' solicitor that the Sheriff had 'the power of the Countrey to assist in the execution of the writ' led to the dissolution of crowd protest. The inhabitants of the mining villages around Grindlow were prepared to defend their right to employment with demonstration and threat, but not with the use of armed force against the state. When the Sheriff's officers returned on 2 August 1738, they encountered no resistance and took the mine 'by force'.

The mine-owners came to a settlement with Lord Cullen in 1749, upon his agreement to more reasonable terms for the continuation of deep mining in Grindlow. The ordinary working miners, of course, gained nothing from that compromise. They and their families had been persuaded into action on the mine-owners' behalf out of a mutual interest in the protection of the right of free mining. Although the miners may have 'lost' in their action against what they saw as an eroding of free mining custom by the unified agreement of mine and rights owners, the result of the action was all part of the growing movement towards establishing a more recognised system of wage earning by skilled workers in an industry of national importance.

No further reference to the mine of any significance has been found until 1877 when it is recorded that 12 tons of lead ore was produced

1820: A cartoon by British illustrator George Cruikshanks titled 'The Law's Delay: Reading The Riot Act 1820'.

(Hulton Archive/Getty Images)

followed by 263 tons in 1879 , 252 tons in 1880, 510 tons in 1882, and 139 tons in 1883 – implying that the mine had only been opened up again when the steam-powered pumping engine had been installed to help draianage.

The final shaft work carried out on site of Silence Mine was reported to have been done by Leonard Maltby, Manager of the Mill Dam Mining Co. The geologist, A Strahan, mentions in his Notebook that:

> 5th February 1880 a shaft was being sunk under the direction of Maltby, being 54 fathoms 4 feet through shale and 33 fathoms in limestone. The best ground was said to be at 25 to 40 fathoms (150-240 ft.) below the top of the limestone, the sole of the shaft being at 378 feet with sumps to 87 fathoms.

In spite of preliminary establishing of watermarks by the Stoke Soughers in Speed Grove it is unlikely that Stoke Sough ever reached this group of mines, either because of the geology or financial caution of the owners. If ever it had been possible to drain them to greater depth than by mechanical means to the Silence Shale Gate then there may well have been a less ignominious end for Silence Mine.

In the Brooke-Taylor documents there is a letter written by Robert How on 17th January 1883 refering to Silence Mine:

> 'Low price of ore and water in mines. Leonard Maltby and one of the miners had a serious accident. They were securing old bunnings and without warning it fell on them in Silence Mine. Leonard Maltby leg broken in several places and the other man several ribs broken. Thinks water will overpower Silence.'

The original shaft at Silence must have 'run in', (that is, collapsed) before 1880. Mr John Howe at Ladywash mine told D A Nash that his father worked at Silence Mine. Nash assumes this was before the first shaft collapsed because Howe says that workmen noticed a bulge in the ginging (stone lining of the upper part of the shaft) and sent for Mr Leonard Maltby, Manager of the Mill Dam Mining Co. who apparently commented that the shaft would have collapsed before they could get back. This proved to be the case.

The end for Silence came quite dramatically. The Derbyshire Times of 13th February 1886 reported that on Saturday the 6th February 1886:

> 'Silence Mine owned by the Mill Dam Mining Co., and having been standing idle for 14 months, the shaft collapsed when the shaft timbers rotted and the subsidence continued until Tuesday and sheds and various plant was precipitated into the hole.'

Excavation of the 'arched' building revealed that it may originally have housed some kind of 'bob' or rocking mechanism – see detail right of 'arc' score marks on the wall.

The hollow which until recently was all that remained of the collapsed shaft of Silence Mine, now filled with spoil from the archaeological dig.

Dr John Barnatt, Senior Survey Archaeologist for the PDNPA, at work on the Silence Mine site.

Peak District Mines Historical Society volunteers begin excavations on the Silence Mine site

After several sessions of digging by the PDMHS volunteers, the anatomy of Silence Mine site begins to reveal itself. The steam engine would have sat on the mass of masonry, top centre. On the right are the coal bunkers, close to the road for easy charging, and centre left is the bed of the boiler, concave to take its shape. Below this is a passageway and drain, and the photograph is taken close to where the chimney may have been situated.

Old Grove Mine

Silence Mine is the last eastward mine on the Hucklow vein within the boundaries of the modern parish of Great Hucklow, in a parcel of land jointly managed by the parishes of Foolow and Great Hucklow as a nature reserve and heritage site. One other mine also lies within this site – Old Grove Mine, (in the Liberty of Foolow) the records of which give some insight into how the mines of the Edge were manned and operated.

Old Grove Mine, had several names including Wright's Edge or Foolow Pasture Mine, but the most popular name was 'Have Adventur' and the vein at the time was referred to as 'Have Adventur Vein', while the same vein further east at Middleton's Engine was known as Middleton Engine Vein and when the whole continuity of the vein was established it all became Hucklow Edge Vein.

Kirkham tells us:

'Old Grove Shaft was sunk about 1711 or a little earlier by Richard Bagshawe and partners – the Great Vein was proved to continue east from the Foolow–Grindlow ground, and for a time it was called Have at a Venture Vein'.

A shale gate was driven to this mine, as was the case with virtually all of the mines east of Silence. The shale gate here was known as 'Old Grove Sough', but was also referred to as 'The Miners Sough' – and the surface evidence of this is marked by the spoil hillocks which trace the course of the sough in the field below. It is considered to have reached the Have Adventur Vein by about 1713.

An analysis was made of the labour force for a period ending March 30th 1759. There were 13 Copers – a leading miner with three or four partners, labourers, haulers, sump winders etc., contracted for work in and about the mine. They used a common Carter, or Jagger Man, with horses to take the ore from the mine and to bring in raw materials: theirs was John Furniss. They had candles from John Downs, and the services of one, sometimes two Blacksmiths, Thomas Froggatt and John Barber. It is assumed that most of the men worked underground, though the various sons mentioned may have been boys, sometimes helping the women, but often used to keep the levels clean. Records at various mines suggest that the levels and especially the shale–gates were constantly being cleaned of loose rocks etc., during the working life of the mine. The women for the most part would be washing and dressing the ore, but they occasionally worked down the mine also.

Old Grove Mine, according to the Wolley Collection manuscripts, was about 200 yards deep, and places in the mine were Hard Door, Old Lib Sump, John Hatfield's Sump, Gregory Sump, Blackwell Sump and Timperley Sump.

Butler's Old Engine or New Grove, the next mine in the Foolow Liberty also had its shale-gate like the others and this one is thought to go into Old Grove Sough, or alternatively to have been run into swallets.

A view from above the Silence Heritage Site showing the spoil heaps marking the line of the 'Miner's Sough'

A Note on Stoke Sough

The story of Stoke Sough and Magclough Sough is fascinating and is told in detail by Dr JH Rieuwerts in his *Leadmining in Derbyshire, History, Development and Drainage Vol 1*.

A large sough known as Stoke Sough was begun in the 1720s (which drained into the River Derwent near Stoke Hall). It was intended to drain all mines along the Eyam Edge towards Hucklow so in the 1730s water marks were made in mines all along the Edge. Those in Old Edge Mine were made at 486 feet. By 1738 the work had cost £11,000 – £12,000. The sough was constructed without any composition (payment) agreement with the owners of the mines along the Edge which seems somewhat foolhardy considering the cost of such a huge and difficult engineering project and that their 'bitterest enemies', Richard Bagshawe and partners, were at the same time driving Magclough Sough also with the object of discovering the Hucklow Edge Old Vein. Inevitably disputes arose over payment and the owners blocked up the sough in 1738 and did not reopen it until 1747. The sough partners or shareholders included Henry Thornhill of Stanton Hall, Francis Sitwell, James and William Milnes and Richard Marples, Auditor to the Dean and Chapter of St. Paul's Cathedral. As it turned out the sough became more of a liability than an asset.

An interesting document in the Bagshawe Collection says:

'the level (horizontal passage for drainage) through the Cranch (a difficult piece of ground to work through and useful for support) at Bradshaws Engine Mine in the Foolow Liberty to be carried on by Stoke Soughers and they are immediately to be put in possession of half mere of ground on each side of the stalch (uncut piece of ground) at the west end of Old Edge Grove which is not meant to convey the property from the miners but to enable the Soughers to prevent that stalch from being cut through to let the water off'

signed by James Mower, Aymer Rich, Joseph Clay, John Spencer and N Twigg Esq.

This suggests that the sough was expected to reach the Grindlow Liberty. Old Edge Grove could refer to Old Grove Mine in the Grindlow liberty rather than to Old Edge mine in the Hucklow Liberty .

It might be wondered why the miners did not cut through the cranch (left by the old miners between the Eyam and Grindlow mines) in order to relieve the water on the Grindlow side. It has been suggested that perhaps they dared not for fear of flooding their eastern workings, that is, until there was somewhere for the water to go. Stoke Sough was driving at the time and they appear to have had every intention of cutting through Bradshaw's 'Cranch' to dewater the Grindlow Mines. But owing to a dispute, no agreement had been made between the soughers and the miners before the Stoke Sough work started, and the Grindlow miners were not of a mind to pay composition on not yet dewatered ground.

By 1753 more trouble occurred. As the Grindlow miners still resisted the payment of composition the Stoke Sough partners, who had put workmen in Bradshaw Engine (Mine) to drive a level through the cranch, agreed as follows:

'We, whose names are subscribed below, do hereby agree and order, that the works which are driving or making at the cranch in Bradshaw Engine Title, shall from henceforth cease to be further driven or wrought until such time as agreement be reached in the several mines lying eastwardly of the old groove in Wright's Edge – Old Grove or Have Adventur'.

Once the owners of the Grindlow mines agreed to pay $1/_8$th of the freed ore got, and the water marks made, then it was settled that the Soughers would drive through the cranch at their sole expense, but seeing it was in the wet part of the season, they would also put the water mark one fathom lower than the present standing water level.

Reckonings below the water mark were made at Speed Mine on July 15th 1753, and 'composition' was paid to the soughers by the Speed miners on 2nd July 1757, presumably in anticipation that the cranch would be completely cut through. This does not seem to have happened,

Rieuwerts thinks that the sough never reached the Grindlow Liberty. Certainly Silence Mine continued to have problems with drainage, and there are no further reckonings yet seen for composition payments.

10. The Life of the Miners

Written by Liz Greenfield based on research by Christine Bucknell, Liz Greenfield and Alan Jones.

The year is 1861. Great Hucklow is one of a scattered group of villages, surrounded by evidence of the lead mining which provides a living for most of its inhabitants, as it has for centuries. The cottages on either side of the main road are small and mostly inhabited by miners. The road is a dirt road, dusty in summer and muddy in winter. Animals graze on the green that borders the road and carts struggle to avoid the ruts that their wheels make in the mud.

Joseph Bradwell lives in the village with his wife Ann and their seven children; the oldest is 17 and the youngest 11 months. Joseph is a lead miner and so are his eldest son, Thomas, and his ten year old son, Robert. Joseph was born in Bradwell but possibly moved to Great Hucklow when he married Ann Longden, daughter of the village shoemaker. Certainly all his children were born in Great Hucklow. He and his large family are living with Ann's widowed mother, Mary.

Benjamin Wragg is also a lead miner but he lives across the valley in Little Hucklow. He is 20 and living in his father's house. His father, also called Benjamin, farms 60 acres. His brother, William, 25 years his senior, works on the farm with his father. William also lives in the house with his wife, and two children. (1)

The purpose of our research was to answer two questions. What was life like for a lead miner and his family? What effect did the failure of the lead mines have on the miners and their communities? To answer these questions and to learn about the lives of Joseph and Benjamin, and the other miners who worked in the parish, we had to gather information from a variety of sources.

Until the nineteenth century little detailed information is available but clues from different sources provide a general picture. There was a census every ten years from 1801. The census recorded the number of inhabitants in each town and village and listed the number in each occupation. In 1841 the names of the people living in each house were recorded for the first time. From 1851 we were able to discover the names and ages of all members of each family, their relationships to the head of the family, their places of birth and their occupations. The parish registers, directories, the school log book, newspapers, maps, photographs, wills, diaries and letters were also valuable. First we had to search for relevant information. Then we had to fit each piece of information into its place as if into a jigsaw puzzle.

We are fortunate to have three extremely valuable resources: the diary of a Bradwell miner, Jabez Bradwell, written between 1877 and 1886, and *Bradwell Ancient and Modern* a book written by Seth Evans in 1912. We have drawn heavily on both these books. In 1906 S O Addy who owned the small manor house in the village wrote an article called *Little Hucklow: Its Customs and Old Houses* for the *Derbyshire Archaeological Journal*.

The little diary of Jabez Bradwell was found by one of his descendants in an attic in the loft of the house where Jabez used to live. It has been transcribed and published by Bradwell Historical Society and gives us more insight into the life of a miner than any other document.

Seth Evans is listed as a 12 year old textile worker in the Bradwell census of 1871. He was three years younger than Jabez Bradwell. In 1912 Seth Evans wrote about the history of Bradwell and about the people he knew and events he had witnessed.

Addy used the manor house in Little Hucklow as a summer residence. He provides valuable information about village life and customs.

Bradwell, a much larger village, is only three miles down the valley. The miners of Bradwell and the miners of our villages must have shared many experiences. We soon became aware of the movement between the villages. Bradwell miners worked in Hucklow mines and Hucklow miners in Bradwell mines.

Summary

For hundreds of years, lead mining was a central part of the life of the villages. There were lean years when life was hard but also times when lead prices were high and many of the miners made a reasonable living. Most miners did not rely totally on lead but also had small crofts where they could grow vegetables and keep a cow. Families could add to their incomes by weaving cotton, often at home. Even in the good times the miners' standard of living was spartan compared with the comforts of today but they were independent, proud people. They provided for their families by their own physical labours.

During the second half of the nineteenth century this way of life was lost, never to return. The independent miner was beaten by the need for expensive machinery and increasing competition from abroad. There was still lead to be mined but the Derbyshire miners could not match the lower prices of first Spanish and then Australian lead. The miners could no longer make a living from lead.

The Life of Miners

Addy paints a rosy picture. Writing in 1906 he says that 'the old men and women look back with regret to the days of their youth and manhood when, as lead miners and little free-holders, they worked short hours in the mines, kept a cow or two and were happy as the day is long'.

This can be only part of the picture. There were times when lead prices were low and poverty extreme. There was no welfare state to protect the miners and having to go into the workhouse was a real fear.

Small pieces of information give us enough glimpses into the lives of the villagers to understand that their poverty was often desperate. In 1641 the population of the Hucklows had risen to 600. Of these, 61% were dependent on lead mining; about half were copers (miners who were paid wages). In 1664, 74% of Little Hucklow residents were too poor to pay the hearth tax, which meant that they had only one hearth. In Great Hucklow it was 84%. (2)

In 1830 a London newspaper, the Sun, which has no connection with today's paper of the same name, published an account of a meeting in Bradwell to plan help for the families suffering from the results of low wages in the lead industry. 'It is impossible to conceive the vast depth of misery that exists . . . many of these poor sufferers had their children in bed when visited, whose bedclothes had not a vestige of either linen or flannel about them, but was composed of wrappers and old clothes; others had not a little of fire.'(3) People living in Bradwell and the neighbourhood subscribed almost £50 (about £3,500 now) which was spent on 'coal, meats and blankets'. (6)

Usually the vulnerable were looked after by their families. Widows, with no occupation, lived with employed sons and daughters. Small children, whose parents had died or were working away, lived with grandparents, uncles or aunts. It was only when kinship support broke down that people were listed as paupers or were forced into the Union Workhouse in Bakewell. In 1841 John Howe was a lead miner in Great Hucklow. Ten years later, aged 74 and a widower, he was recorded in the 1851 census as a former lead miner and a pauper. This meant that he received help from the parish. In 1841 Ann Blackwell was a child of eight, living in Great Hucklow with her mother, who was a cotton weaver, and her younger brother Samuel. Samuel died in 1845 and a year later her mother died, leaving Ann on her own.(7) We have been unable to find her in the 1851 census but by 1861 she was one of several boarders in the house of Ann Bramwell in Litton and was a cotton factory worker. Her story is sad; by 1871 she was in the union workhouse in Bakewell. She was still there in 1881 and by 1891 she was blind.(1)

Houses

Initially the miners built their cottages along the more easily accessible lead veins. Flat land for building was scarce so many of the houses were built on slopes as in Little Hucklow, Bradwell and Grindlow. The village street in Great Hucklow is relatively flat as it is in Windmill. As Bradwell was so much bigger and more important as a mining village there was pressure on space for houses and so there was close infilling; in the Hucklows the pressure was not the same and the villages developed along the main streets.

The larger houses in the villages were usually occupied by tenant farmers and the smaller cottages by lead miners and tradesmen who rented their properties. The miners would use stone from the local quarries and build their own houses. Many houses would have a croft behind them where the occupants would grow vegetables and

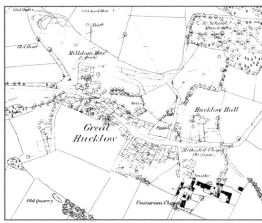

19th Century maps of the villages of Little and Great Hucklow

keep a cow. The more prosperous miners would invest in property but would often rent a house themselves. They would let their own houses or allow their children to live in them. Some bought land and became farmers, retaining their shares in mines.

The early houses in the fourteenth and fifteenth centuries were built round cruck beams with a stone or thatched roof. The eighteenth and nineteenth century houses had a similar layout but they were of solid stone construction with stone roofs supported by oak purlins (beams the length of the roof).

A lead miner's cottage usually had a living room and scullery/pantry downstairs and two bedrooms upstairs. Conditions were primitive. The cottages were dark and draughty and the bedrooms usually had no ceilings so that the roof tiles and rafters were exposed. Ladders gave access to upstairs but were gradually replaced by narrow stone or wood staircases. Doors at the bottom and top helped to reduce draughts, provide some privacy and conserve heat. The houses were smoky from the fires. Most had flag floors. Any toilets were outside and possibly shared with other cottages.

Furnishing was basic. There were wooden chairs and tables; clothing and other possessions were kept in oak chests. A mirror, tall clock or wash stand, with a jug and bowl, were luxuries. So too was a piano or musical instrument but some miners had them. Rugs made of knotted rags, wool or sacking covered some of the flag floors. Plates were of wood, tin or earthenware.

Beds were made of wooden slats with a mattress

and pillows filled with feathers. The headboard and the end of the bed were of brass or wood. There were holes in the walls for storing belongings. There were eight rectangular holes in the walls of Addy's manor house, the largest being 1ft 6 ins square with a depth of 1ft. Three of the holes were in the room above the hall, one at the head of the winding staircase, one in the hall and three in the kitchen. Many cottages still have these holes in their walls.

The houses had small windows and were dark. Lighting was by oil lamp or candles. Oilmen delivered paraffin. Food was cooked on a wood burning range or in pots hung over an open fire. If the miners could not afford coal they would use turfs and wood for heating and cooking which would make their cottages very smoky. They collected heather from the moors to use as kindling. Addy had seen women in Little Hucklow 'dragging a great bundle of kindling with a rope for a mile or more'.

The miners spent most of their income on food and drink. They tried to be self-sufficient; they grew vegetables and often kept a cow and chickens on their strip of land or croft. Rings in a beam, where flitches of bacon and salted pork were hung, still remain in some cottages. Jabez Bradwell records killing a pig, which he cut into joints. It weighed 15 stone and nine lbs. Later he hung up the flitches, which had been salted in the cellar.

Water was a problem, especially in Little Hucklow. The lads and lasses from the village would fetch water from a spring in Sinings Lane. They carried water in 'burn cans' placed on padded round cushions, like quoits, on their heads. (5)

Many of the miners' wives made their own butter, cheese and bread. These, together with eggs and milk, were kept as cool as possible in a scullery or cellar.

Clothes

Clothes were hand washed, using homemade soap, and then put through a hand wringer. They were dried on a wooden frame that hung above the kitchen range and ironed with a flat iron which was heated on the range or fire.

Women made clothes for themselves and the children, using coarse woollen, flannel, cotton, calico and linen. They wore print dresses, aprons and shawls. Children would have 'hand me downs' or clothes altered from adults'. Those who were better off had their dresses made. The sisters Ann and Mary Ash were listed as dressmakers in Great Hucklow in the 1861 census.

Richard Cheetham and Edwin Longden were shoemakers and Matthew Gregory and John Eyre were tailors in Great Hucklow in 1861. Men had clothes made by the local tailor or, in the late nineteenth century, bought 'off the peg' on the Moor in Sheffield, which was cheaper. They wore suits with waistcoats, a coarse shirt and necktie. They also wore caps and long loose overcoats, called Ulsters, which were made of rough cloth. Jabez Bradwell bought a coat and vest from Hides on the Moor in Sheffield for 16s 6d (about £56

now) and later bought a suit for £2.(6) His brother Stephen had to help him find the money for that; he lent him 30 shillings. Most people would have two sets of clothes, one for best and one for everyday. Suits were worn for best first, including church on Sunday, and then for work. Photographs show the miners wearing jackets, trousers and waistcoats of coarse cloth. They also wore shirts, neckties and caps or Bradda hats. These were hard hats invented and made in Bradwell from the early eighteenth century. Miners wore leather shoes with wooden soles and iron rings round the soles for protection. Many, but not all, had beards.

Village Life

Jabez Bradwell, Seth Evans and Addy tell of villages full of life and energy. W G Hoskins, in his book Local History in England, quotes Eric Gill who described the 'old world' which was to change so dramatically in the second half of the nineteenth century. 'It was not a primitive world, it was not an uncivilised world, and above all it was not an uncultured world. All the primary needs of humanity, material and spiritual, were met and met adequately.' It was, however, a hard world.

Most of a family's needs were met within the village. In 1861 John Gooldan was a joiner and wheelwright and the brothers Nathaniel and Benjamin Sommerset were carpenters. William Waterhouse was a blacksmith. William Chapman,

Group of local miners c1865 ar Rake Head Mine, Moss Rake. Includes Robert Howe, Barmaster with measures and Robert Ashton, with dog.

a shopkeeper, employed Samuel Dawson as his carter. William Hancock was a tea dealer as well as a lead miner. Twenty years earlier, in 1841, John Naylor had been a soap manufacturer and John Bower a glass manufacturer but by 1861 they had long left the village.

The church provided much of the social activity in the village. Jabez Bradwell sang in the Bradwell church choir and went to bible class, missionary and temperance meetings. Church teas were popular. Jabez records going to teas at both St Barnabas and the Methodist chapel. He usually paid a shilling (about £3.50 now) for his tea. (6) He also went to other villages for services, including Castleton, Hope and Peak Forest. He records going to a concert at the church school.

Jabez also mentions the annual village flower show in August and records with pride that his sister Annie won a prize for her wild flower arrangement.

He played cricket for Bradwell against Peak Forest and Hathersage.

Wakes and fairs were important; we know that the school closed so that the children could attend. The fairs provided an opportunity for buying and selling. Jabez bought teaspoons at Tideswell fair for 8d (about £2.30 now) and penholders for 4d. He sold a cow at Hope fair for £22 10s (about £1,550 now) and bought another for £14 10s. (6) Earlier he had recorded the sale of a cow by his grandfather at Hope market.

In the nineteenth century both the Hucklows had their wakes weeks, Great Hucklow in August and Little Hucklow the second week in September. Addy described one Little Hucklow custom: the villagers painted their stone window frames with a bright colour, the colour being changed, each year, for wakes week. When Addy wrote his account, his windows on the south side of the Manor House were painted yellow but he was convinced that the original colours were red and blue as he had scraped off layers of paint before reaching those colours. The last colour to be used was probably green as traces of that colour remain on some stone window frames today.

According to Addy there was mischief in the village on the eve of wakes week. Gates were lifted off their hinges, brooms disappeared and carts were driven down the hill until they ended up in the wet places at the bottom of Sinings Lane. Seth Evans describes the same sort of mischief in Bradwell on Christmas Eve. He disapproved. Cattle and sheep were lost after gates had been removed and property was damaged. After the police arrived in Bradwell the practice declined and by 1912, when Seth Evans was writing, there was very little 'mischief' compared with former times.

There were other customs. Addy describes how a rope was tied across the road to impede a wedding party on its way to the chapel until the bridegroom paid a toll. This also happened in Castleton, Bradwell, Eyam, Edale and Bamford. Addy doesn't say who got the money but Seth Evans thought it was spent later at the nearest public house.

On Shrove Tuesday, whoever was last to get up was called a 'bed churl' and was swept with a broom. This must have been an unpleasant experience; Addy claimed that some stayed up all-night to avoid being a 'bed churl'. The last miner to get to work on Shrove Tuesday was carried on a pole and 'tipped down th' hillock'. One miner hated this so much that he stabbed one of his persecutors with a knife.

On Palm Sunday the villagers of Little Hucklow laid a ring of palms (the buds or catkins of the common sallow) round Silver well which was on the east side of the village. This is the only dressing of a well mentioned by Addy and he emphasises that no flowers were used.

But Seth Evans refers to the former practice of dressing the Bradwell wells; they had been 'beautifully decorated with flowers' until 50 years before. In the past, Bradwell had also had its garland day, similar to Castleton's. A man rode around the village with a huge garland on his head. The band led the procession and there was dancing in Towngate.

Although the miners were religious, some remnants of pagan rites survived. In Little Hucklow on Easter Monday the men 'cucked up' or lifted up the women and on Easter Tuesday it was the women's turn to try to 'cuck up' the men. Addy suggests that this was originally a magical rite to make the crops grow; the belief was that imitating the rise of the crops from the earth by jumping would make them grow. The custom in Bradwell was slightly different. On Easter Monday the girls

was recorded in the census as a farmer and a Wesleyan local preacher.

Robert Shenton, minister of the Unitarian chapel in Great Hucklow, had been born in Ashburton, Devon and had originally come to Bradwell, to preach Primitive Methodism. He preached the sermon at the opening of the Primitive Methodist chapel in Little Hucklow in 1826. Later he became a Unitarian and was pastor at the Unitarian Chapel in Flagg, moving to the chapels in Bradwell and Great Hucklow on the resignation of the Rev Robert Naylor in 1840.(3)

Primitive Methodism spread to nearby villages, including Little Hucklow, from Bradwell where the first chapel in the area had been established. The enthusiasm of the people of Little Hucklow was proved when the Sunday school was built by public subscription in 1857.

Movement

We tend to think that people in the past moved little, staying in the village where they were born surrounded by family and lifelong friends. But the censuses show that many people left the villages to look for work and others moved in. Often people would return to their own villages after several moves. Most of the movement shown in the 1861 census was between the villages themselves: the Hucklows, Windmill and Grindlow. Some came from further afield: Eyam, Tideswell, Bradwell, Castleton, Winster and Sheldon. It was rare for anyone living in our villages to have been born out of Derbyshire. Particularly useful are the birth places of the children in a family; they show where the family has lived and can give some idea of the timing of the family's moves. William Swindell, a 58-year-old widower, was a lead miner in Great Hucklow. He had been born in Stanton Lees, his daughter in Monyash, one of his grandsons in Ashford and the other in Great Hucklow. Nathaniel Wilson, a lead miner in Great Hucklow, unusually came from outside Derbyshire. He had been born in Essex. His wife was born in Bradwell and his five children in Little Hucklow. Richard Cheetham, a shoemaker, was born in Lancashire and his wife in the City of London. His two older children were born in Litton but he was in Great Hucklow for the birth of his five younger children.

Jabez Bradwell tells us much about the social events of the area. He went to the wakes and fairs in other villages, including Castleton, Tideswell and Hathersage. He travelled with the church choir and the village band. On Tuesday 2 June 1877 he went with the band to Hathersage and the following day to Taddington. In September that year the Dove Holes Band played at the Bulls Head in Bradwell.

Early contact with other areas came through religion. The Apostle of the Peak, who had been born in Litton, studied at Cambridge University, served as assistant minister in Attercliffe and was ordained in Chesterfield. In 1652 he was appointed to the living in Glossop. After his ejection from Glossop he lived in Chapel-in-le-Frith and from here travelled to Great Hucklow every Sunday to preach.

The Hucklows were also a part of the Methodist network. Bradwell had early ties with Methodists in Sheffield. Sarah Moore, a member of the Methodist society in Hallam, regularly walked from Sheffield to Bradwell to preach. Seth Evans records the visit of William Green from Rotherham in 1760. In the nineteenth century circuit plans meant that local preachers moved through the villages.

White's Sheffield Gazetteer of 1851 lists Benjamin Turner, formerly a lead miner, as a carrier to Sheffield. Kelly's 1864 Directory shows how the world was opening up. Letters came through Bakewell and the nearest money order office was in Tideswell. Benjamin Turner was going to Sheffield on Monday, Wednesday and Friday and to Buxton on Tuesday, Thursday and Saturday. John Bagshaw also ran a carrier service. He went to the Parrot Inn, Sheffield on a Saturday, returning the same day. The 1881 Directory states that the nearest railway station was at Millers Dale where trains from there went to Manchester and Derby. The Dore and Chinley line, bringing rail access to Sheffield, was not opened until the 1890s. A 1916 directory announced that parcels could now be addressed to Great Hucklow 'Hope Station, per milkman'.

The decline in lead mining

In many ways the lives of the villagers improved towards the end of the nineteenth century. More children went to school and some had the chance of going on to the grammar school in Tideswell.

Their health was better, largely through improved water supplies and health care. The birth rate went down but people were living longer. But the lead mines were failing and the old life disappearing. The small miners had been defeated by the need for expensive machinery to deal with the problem of water in the mine and by the fall in lead prices. Lead prices had fallen before but this time they would not recover.

It happened so quickly. Kelly's Directory of 1864 gives mining as the principal employment in Great Hucklow. In 1881 the directory says 'mining is still the principal employment.' A new directory in 1887, only six years later, states: 'Mining was the principal employment of the inhabitants but the mines are at present closed.' The lead industry, which had provided employment for most people in the area for hundreds of years, had gone. The villages were hit hard. The miners had a choice; they had to find whatever work they could in the area or leave to find work elsewhere.

Jabez Bradwell's diary reveals the plight of one lead mining family. Thomas, Jabez's grandfather, had prospered as a lead miner and by 1871 was farming 180 acres. When he died in 1886 he left his four sons the houses they were living in and money to his daughters. His mines and shares in mines were to be divided equally between his sons and daughters. Charles, Thomas's son and father of Jabez, died just six years later. He left his house and barns, his mines and shares in mines to his wife for her lifetime. On her death everything, except his shares in Dirtlow Mine which he left to Jabez, was to be sold to pay his debts. (16)

In the 1881 Bradwell census both Charles and Jabez Bradwell claimed to be miners. They certainly still owned mines but were earning little from them. Along with many others from the mining villages, Jabez left home to look for work elsewhere. He went to Stocksbridge to work for Samuel Fox, a Bradwell man, who had founded a steel and umbrella works in Stocksbridge. When times were hard he encouraged young men from Bradwell to go and work for him. Jabez recorded his own arrival in Stocksbridge:

1882
January 31st Came to Stocksbridge Tuesday
February 3rd Began work at Fox's Friday

Jabez stayed in Stocksbridge for two years,

returning to Bradwell in March 1884. He must have longed to get back to Bradwell, although he knew that there was little if any work for him in the family mines.

Two months after his return Jabez's diary shows that he took whatever employment he could find:

1884
June 20th Went in woods for a week 4.½ (pence) hour (about £1.30 now)
July 1st and 2nd In shoemakers shop half day Tues. all Wed 2/6 a day (about £8.50 now) (6)
Started emptying brook Tues
Went in hay same day Cupola
Aug 5th I took 2 cows to Mount Pleasant Tues
15th and 16th Mowed old OBA's field same day
21st Cutting corn in meadow
25th and 26th Filling shaft up Furniss Grove Mon and Tues
26th Putting things in stable Tuesday
27th Started breaking stone Eden Hall Wed

Jabez managed to get work stone breaking, sometimes with his uncle Stephen. He was also paid for lighting the school boiler but this was only work for the winter months. He was paid 10 shillings (about £34.50 now) for three months' work.(6) In spite of his efforts times were hard for his family. At Christmas 1885 they were unable to afford the traditional posset, made from warmed milk and ale and spiced with nutmeg. On 30 December he went to a tea and concert; he was given a free tea. On 30 January the vicar gave the family a ticket for 3 cwt of 'dole coal'.

Joseph Walker of Little Hucklow, another lead miner, also had to get whatever work he could. His father was a lead miner and so were his brothers. In 1891 he was employed as a general labourer and ten years later, at 63, was a stonebreaker on the roads.

Joseph Chapman was one of those who left the area to seek work elsewhere. He was five in 1841 and was living in Little Hucklow. By 1871 he, and his wife Mary from Bretton, were in Foolow. Joseph was a lead miner. Ten years later he was a gas maker in Edale. Four of his children worked in the cotton mill and the family lived in a mill cottage. He was still in Edale in 1891 but by then was a general labourer. His sons, Alen, Anthony and Robert were labourers on the railway.

Another Joseph Chapman, born about 1840,

was also in Little Hucklow in 1841. In 1851 he was living with his father and working on his father's farm of 100 acres. He was still there in 1861 and 1871. His father died in 1879.(7) Joseph's older brother Martin was a farmer in Little Hucklow in 1881 but had only 13 acres. We don't know why the farm had lost so many acres: perhaps the land had been sold to pay debts. The farm would be unable to support Joseph as well as Martin and his family so in 1881 Joseph was a labourer and a lodger at Bentslowe, the Eyres' house near Great Hucklow. By 1891 he had left the area and was working as a porter and night relieving officer at Glossop Union Workhouse. Martin remained a farmer in Little Hucklow and was still there in 1901.

How did the families of Joseph Bradwell and Benjamin Wragg, who we met at the beginning of this chapter, fare in this difficult world? In 1871 Joseph was living with his wife Ann, his sons Robert and George and his grandson, Albert who was one year old. By 1881 Ann had died, but he and two of his sons, George and William, were still lead miners. His son Robert had left the village to seek work and was a labourer in a steel works in Hunshelf, near Stocksbridge. In 1891 Robert was living in Snowden Hill, Hunshelf and was a labourer in an iron works. By 1901 he had moved on and was a bricklayer's labourer in Upper Hallam, Sheffield. He lived in Hangingwater Road

with his wife, Ellen.

Joseph's grandson, Albert, also left the village. In 1891 he was 21 and was a labourer on the railway in Edale. He lived in one of the huts built to accommodate the labourers. Ten years later he had moved on to Ardsley in the West Riding with his wife Emma and his daughter, Florence, who was four. He was a 'tunnel excavator-navvy'. Perhaps his prospects had improved; his house was large enough to take a boarder, William Lattimore, who was also a tunnel excavator.

Joseph remained in the village and in 1891 was 'employed as a lead miner'. His granddaughter, Florence, who was 19, was his housekeeper. She had a three month-old son, Thomas. Florence had married Frederick Wildgoose from Sheldon and may have lived with her grandfather while Frederick was looking for work. Florence and Frederick were together in 1901 with their children, James who was six and Ellen who was four. It is likely that Thomas had not survived. The family was living at 71 Bennett Street, Buxton. Frederick was a 'scavenger labourer'.

Benjamin Wragg stayed in Little Hucklow. After his father's death in the 1860s he became a lead miner and farmer. In his will of 1865, Benjamin senior divided his land amongst his three sons and left £20 to each of his daughters. (15) Benjamin's wife Hannah had died in her early thirties. By 1891

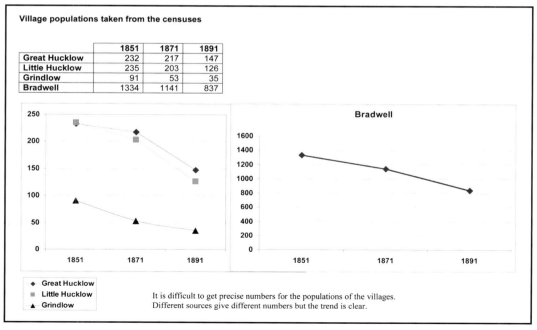

Village populations taken from the censuses

	1851	1871	1891
Great Hucklow	232	217	147
Little Hucklow	235	203	126
Grindlow	91	53	35
Bradwell	1334	1141	837

- ◆ Great Hucklow
- ■ Little Hucklow
- ▲ Grindlow

It is difficult to get precise numbers for the populations of the villages. Different sources give different numbers but the trend is clear.

he had re-married; his wife Susannah had been born in Hyde. He was still a farmer but in 1901 at the age of 60 he was a 'farmer and limestone quarryman'.

The full effect on the villages is hard to imagine. The population fell and houses became empty. Both the Hucklows, and Grindlow lost about a third of their population in the 20 years between 1871 and 1891. Bulmer's directory of 1895 was depressing reading. In Little Hucklow 'empty houses meet the eye on every side and desolation reigns supreme'. In Great Hucklow 'the population has diminished very considerably since the discontinuance of lead mining and the many tenantless houses give the place a saddening aspect'. In 1906 Addy, writing about Little Hucklow, tells us that the 'cessation of the industry (lead mining) has been followed by the decay of the village; nearly a third of the houses are unoccupied and ruinous'.

How did the villagers cope with such devastating change? It is hard to imagine the affect of this exodus on the communities. Many of the villagers watched their young people leave to find work elsewhere. Houses were empty, shops had closed, former lead miners had become labourers and poverty was a reality for many. But their churches remained, providing support and practical help. The development of the limestone quarries to feed the increasing demand for new roads gave some hope of future employment.

It is 2008. Great Hucklow is still one of a scattered group of villages. Some of us live in the old lead miners' cottages which still line the streets but few of us work in the villages. We have made two cottages into one; we have piped water and electricity, central heating and washing machines. We have carpeted over the old flag stones. Lawns and gardens replace the vegetable plots and the areas where cows and chickens were kept. We have garages for our cars rather than barns for our tools and our animals. Many old farmhouses are now just houses. The shops where the miners bought their food and clothes closed long ago. Only one pub remains and one church. But the lead miners have left their mark. Old mine shafts and old rakes surround us. We use their footpaths, walk on their village greens, and go to their church and to their school. We hear their stories and begin to understand something of the lives of these proud people who worked so hard and lived such spartan lives. The lead miners.

References and Background Reading

1   Census returns; 1841to 1901
2   Derbyshire Hearth Tax assessments 1664
3   Seth Evans, *Bradwell: Ancient and Modern* (1912)
4   *The Jabez Bradwell Diary 1877-1886* Published by Bradwell Historical Society 1996
5   S O Addy, Little Hucklow: Its Customs and Old Houses *Derbyshire Archaeological Journal*, Volume 28
6   Approximate money conversions based on 2006 prices
7   Births, Marriages and Deaths Indexes for England and Wales from1837
8   Jennifer Gardiner, Great Hucklow – A Lead Mining Village in the Nineteenth Century: Population and Occupations, *Derbyshire Miscellany*, Volume 10 Autumn 1983
9   *The Journeys of Celia Fiennes* (from 1685 – 1703)
10   Daniel Defoe, *A Tour through the Whole Island of Great Britain* (1724-1726)
11   J S Goodhart *Lead Mining An Introduction* (1985)
12   Jack Binks Great Hucklow Remembered 2004
13   Log book of Great Hucklow School 1872 to 1906
14   S E Archer, *The History of St Barnabas School Bradwell* (1972)
15   John Wesley's Journal
16   Wills of Thomas and Charles Bradwell of Bradwell and Benjamin Wragg of Little Hucklow in the Derbyshire Record Office
17   Directories: White's Sheffield Gazetteer 1851, Kelly's Directories 1864, 1881and 1887, Bulmer's Directory 1895 and 1897

Female Miners in 'The Mirror of Literature'

This is an extract from an article which appeared in 'The Mirror of Literature, Amusement and Instruction' of Saturday March 7th, 1829 (Vol. XIII No 359), and based on a tour of the Peak District of Derbyshire by the author.

He visited the caves in Castleton and then other mining villages close by to collect geological specimens. The ladies he described, and whose appearance he also drew, might just be typical of inhabitants of the Hucklow Liberties at the time.

Our engraving endeavours to represent the costume of women who work in some of the Derbyshire lead-mines; they are capital figures, to which the pencil can scarcely do justice; indeed, though this sketch was drawn from nature, it conveys but an imperfect idea of beings, (nondescripts) who would assuredly delight Cruikshank. The dress of these women, of whom the writer saw several emerged from mines a few miles from the Peak, seems contrived to secure them from the cold and wet attendant upon their employment. The head is much enwrapped, and the features nearly hidden, in a muffling of handkerchiefs, over which is put a man's hat, in the manner of the paysannes of Wales, but not near so neat and stylish; besides, the Welsh women are generally handsome, and become the hat; but the case is far different with the fair miners of Derbyshire, at least those whom I saw, who were complete harridans. A man's coat, of coarse gray or dark blue cloth, defends the arms, back, throat, and bosom of each lady from the cold; beneath it, but tucked up all round so as to form a kind of bag, appears a gown of red stuff, which, set off by a bright green petticoat, produces an effect singular and amusing; then come the shoes, at least three inches thick, and long in proportion, bound on to the feet, in some instances, with handkerchiefs, and thongs, and cords: it is a wonder that the women can stir in such unwieldy slippers. Our party had stopped to collect specimens of the lead ore, when the carriages were instantly surrounded by these females, offering ore, zinc, slick-and-slide, and various quartz crystals and fluor spars for sale; some of the women were very old, and one in particular, who had worked in the mine from her youth, was nearly a hundred years of age, yet she was upright and active, and wrinkles alone betrayed the fact.

11. T'Owd Mon Tells His Story

Mr Brian Woodall of Tideswell has performed his re-enactment of T'Owd Mon in schools for over 20 years, and is an active member of PDHMS. The following is transcribed directly from an audio recording made in January 2008.

A typical day for the average miner in t'owd days? Well let's say it's a summers day, and you get up at break of day to go lead mining. The lead mines might be several miles away from where you live in one of these little old villages, and of course the houses that people lived in those days was really primitive. They wouldn't have a proper kitchen. When you got up in the morning you'd perhaps have a swill in a bit of a tub outside, and then for breakfast there might still be some oatmeal left in the barrel and you'd have some porridge, and if you were lucky a bit of fatty bacon to get you going in the day.

So you'd perhaps set off out of the village with your family and up towards the rakes, but you'd be going past your little family farm, and say it's summer, you need to get the hay in, you've mown with a scythe a few days previously, a little field of hay. You may turn that field of hay before you go to work. You've already fed the pigs, because they were very important to the family economy, and you may even have a cow to milk on your way to work, and that kept them going in food even if the price of lead fell.

Now not all of the villages were right close to the mines, a lot of us had to walk several miles every day, to get to the rakes, and the rakes are great long veins, running from east to west, generally, that had been worked for centuries, by the Old Man, our ancestors, so Tideslow rake has been worked perhaps since the fourteen hundreds, so sometimes we're going over the same ground as they had gone over.

The veins run east to west because that's the way that the mineral came up out of the earth. Now up on the rake, where the workings are, you'd perhaps have some very primitive machinery, some buddles, a windlass for winding up stuff from the mine, and perhaps richer mines would have a horse engine for pulling the lead out of the deep shafts. And most of the mines would have a little shed built straight over the top of the climbing

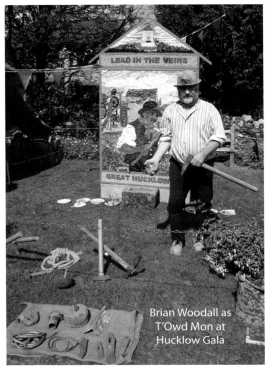

Brian Woodall as T'Owd Mon at Hucklow Gala

shaft and it would have a lock and key on it this shed would, and we'd call it a coe.

So first thing in the morning you'd go and unlock your little shed, your little coe, change into your mining clothes, which you would have hung up inside the coe, overnight. Of course these are still a bit mucky and damp from the previous day, but this is a method whereby you'd keep your outside clothes as dry as possible so that you'd got something to change into when you get out the mine.

So you put your old mucky mining clothes on, you stick your Bradda hat on, this was a thick bowler hat which was made down in the village of Bradwell, made out of rabbit skins or felted wool, but these hats were stiffened with resin and then you got a lump of clay, you stuck it onto the front of the hat and you stuck your candle in that, and that was all the lighting you got when you were climbing down hundreds of feet of ladder ways.

Now quite a lot of villages had chandlers shops, where the candles were made, and they say at Castleton there were the biggest chandler shop there, where they made candles out of waste fat from the slaughter houses. Also the ropes were made locally. In the huge entrance of Peak Cavern, there were several rope making machines inside. So a lot of the stuff was made locally, because to get anything from the town would cost quite a lot of money, so we've got quite a lot of artisans and craftsmen making up the ropes and candles, and the Bradda hats to keep us going.

So you've changed into your clothes, you've checked that you've got enough candles to last you through the day, you've remembered to take a bit of packing up for your dinner, and you've sorted out some black powder, gun powder, in case you need to do any blasting. So then it's a matter of setting off down the ladder ways into the mine. Now this is where it comes very handy, because you've built your little shed right on top of the climbing shaft, and this means that when you come out at night and you're climbing up your climbing shaft it may be howling a gale outside with horizontal sleet, but you're climbing up inside a nice dry little shed. And also with a lock and key hopefully, and that's where you put your lead after it's all been dressed, and waiting for the Barmaster to come and measure it.

So we set off down the ladder ways, very primitive; in some places they had proper ladders, but in others, it was just rungs set into slots on either side of the vein, so you dug deep slots out in the limestone, and jammed rungs into that, and that's what the old lead miner referred to as stemples, and sometimes they didn't even have that, and just went down hand and foot in the foot holes, so it was a bit dangerous.

After you've climbed down several hundred feet of these ladder ways, and also gone across through some cross cuts, which might be pretty tight, you might be crawling through these cross cuts to get to your work – you see we didn't make these mines any bigger than we had to. If you were going through just bare barren rock with no lead in it, you made a smallish tunnel, because black powder was very dear, to make a bigger passage way. So after lots of climbing down and crawling, you come to what we call the fore-field, where you are working at the lead at the present time. Now if you were in the vein, and you'd got all sorts of spar materials in the vein, like the fluorspar, and the barytes, and the galena, the lead ore, this sort of stuff was quite

soft, and you could quite easily pick it down with a slender pick, or you could use wedges, which we call gads. These gads are hammered in and forced the mineral off the walls, and then you try and sort it out. Now, when the minerals came up from deep within the earth, you got fluorspar, calcium fluoride, you've got the barytes, these weren't worth a penny to us the miners, all we wanted was galena, the lead ore. and you really don't want to take these up to the surface, because all you do on the surface is just throw them away. So if we can find an old pocket or a cave system, where we can trim the mineral off the lead ore, and just save the lead ore, and throw the mineral away into one of these old pockets or old cave systems, then we back fill the old cave system with the waste fluorspar and barytes.

Now in those days, kiddies didn't go to school of course, the young lads worked down underground with their dads and uncles, and the daughters had to work out on the surface, either looking after the little farm or helping at the mine. If you've got your young lad with you underground he might do the dragging for you. So you would load your trimmed lead ore onto a little sledge, some sort of basket on a sledge, we call that a corf, and if he's lucky you'd put some wooden planks down on the floor, so that he can drag this corf full of lead a bit easier along the passage way. And he drags it along the passage way until he comes to the main shaft. But the main shaft is a vertical shaft, driven right from daylight, right down into the mine for haulage purposes. Now he arrives at the bottom of the main shaft, and up on the surface the girls and the mothers would perhaps be working an old-fashioned windlass, with big handles on, and what that windlass did was lower some rope or chain down into the mine, and with a bucket or a kibble on the end, and the lad would tip the lead into this iron kibble, or it might be a bit like a wooden barrel, and the ladies on the surface would begin to wind this very heavy lead out of the mine.

In a way the girls and ladies had it worse than the men because they were working out on the surface in the wind and rain, not only hauling the stuff up to the surface, but then they had to trim it, and throw any waste away, and one of the ways of sorting out the lead from the other minerals, was by sieving it; now just imagine sieving it out in tubs of cold water in the winter. But then they'd also got methods of making troughs with water running through it, called a buddle, and you could sort the mineral in this buddle with a rake. Of course up on the surface of the lead mines, there's not much surface water, and you may have to haul barrels of water out of the mine to work this washing process.

Some of the richer lead mines would have a horse engine and that would do away with the ladies having to work the windlass. Now a horse engine has a big flat pulley, which is towed round and round by a couple of horses, and this hauls the lead out of the mine. And also a lead crushing wheel which is driven by a horse, where a horse drives a millstone round a circle, an iron circle, and the operators throw mineral onto the crushing wheel, and that knocks it down, so it can be more easily sorted.

Once on the surface the lead is sorted, and it's pretty pure galena, lead ore, which is very heavy stuff, it's seven times as heavy as water. You were to take that into your little shed, into your little lock up, and look after it, as I say at night you'd turn the key in the lock, to make sure it was safe, and then every now and then the Barmaster, the chief official of the Barmote Court, would come along and would measure your lead for you, because he would decide how much tax you had to pay. After the Barmaster's been and done the official thing, then you can sell your lead on to the smelters. Now these were the lads who really made the money. They were the chaps who took your lead away, and smelted it down, ready to be sent away to the markets. Now, because it's just a compound of lead and sulphur, a very simple compound, it can be roasted in the air, quite simply, and the heat drives off the sulphur, and you're just left with the silvery lead metal. And that can be poured into ingots quite easily, and then be taken away to the market.

Now, hundreds and hundreds of years ago, the way that the lead was smelted, was up in the bole hills. Now on the maps, there's quite a few places called bole hill around here, and that indicates a metal smelt, generally right up on the surface of the top of the hills, and this, we're going back to medieval times now, is where they would have a big pit already dug, facing the west winds, and this

pit would be filled, alternately, with brush wood, and big bolts of timber and then layers and layers of galena, lead ore, and another layer of brush wood and timber, another layer of lead ore, until they filled the pit. Then, when they had a good inkling that the west wind was going to blow for many hours, they would set fire to it, and the heat from all this timber would smelt the lead, drive off the sulphur, and out would come pouring the molten lead, like a little silver river, and then this was cast into ingots. And, on either side of the pour, the ingots were formed in little pits, and some people thought that this looked like a mother pig feeding her little ones, so they were called pigs of lead, these ingots. Much later, of course, we had the more modern reverberatory furnaces, and that was much more efficient, and it didn't have to be done up on the hill top.

Now the point is, that the main market for lead, like most other things, was down in London, and how do you get it from Peak District to London, when the roads are dreadful. The old way of getting it to market, was by, well taking it by mule, or if you were lucky, on a cart, all the way to Bawtry, where it was then put on the River Idle, and then taken to the Trent. From the Trent it went all the way to Hull, there were a lot of lead merchants up at Hull, and then it was put on the ships and sent all the way down the East Coast down to London, where of course a lot of it was sent to the continent. Later on, the entrepreneurs got a lot of money together and they dug the Chesterfield Canal, and so thereafter most of our lead went that way, right along the Chesterfield Canal right up to West Stockwith, where it was loaded into river barges on the Trent, and then taken to Hull that way

Anyway, back underground, our lead miner's been working in the fore-field getting the lead down, but he's decided that he would rather like to drive a cross cut level from where he's working now into a side vein that he knows exists about six or eight yards away to the left, but he's got to drive through the solid rock, and limestone, it's the second hardest rock in Britain, and so for that you have to use gunpowder. So he's taken a small quantity of black powder down with him, and his straw fuses. So him and his son start to drilling, and to start making a cross cut tunnel. So the technique that they use, the drill is just like a long chisel, just with a single blade at the end, perhaps a little bit fish-tailed, but that's all it is. They perhaps need two or three candles at this stage so as you don't hit yourself – take the candle off your hat and stick it in some clay on the wall of the mine, perhaps two or three candles like that, and then the young boy holds the chisel against the rock, the drill bit, and the father strikes the drill with a big hammer, and then the young lad quickly turns it round a quarter of a turn; the father strikes again, turns it round again, strike turn, strike turn, you've got to keep doing that, so that the rock powder comes out of the hole, and also so that the drill bit doesn't start to bind in the very strong rock at the bottom end of the hole. So you keep drilling like that for, it would take best part of an hour to drill in a foot deep and then you need to make a pattern of these holes, perhaps eight or ten holes, so it might take you a couple of days to get all these holes drilled out, so you do the same again drilling a pattern of holes ready to put the explosives in.

After about three holes you're getting a bit tired and hungry, so it's time for something to eat, if you're lucky you might have some oatcake with you that you've made. These are little pancakes made out of the oatmeal, perhaps some cheese from the cow, so you've got cheese and oatcake, and perhaps in winter, when you've killed the pig, you might even have some black pudding to eat with your oatcake. For drink, well, they'd always be a drip of water somewhere in the mine, and if previously you'd taken an old cup down there and stood it under this drip of water, then you'd have something to drink.

So after you'd drilled out eight or ten shot holes, it's then time to clean these shot holes out with a little scraper which we call a crauncher, and that gets rid of all the waste, the limestone dust, and then you start to load in your black powder, a mixture of sulphur and charcoal and saltpetre, you load in your black powder into the hole and then tap it in tight with a wooden rammer, got to be wooden, you've got to avoid sparks by all means at this point, then you put in some clay; you always use quite a lot of clay under ground for making little canals around the mine and you use a lot of clay in the shot firing process. Then you would put in a copper shooting needle and then

pack it all around with clay and ram the clay all around this long shooting needle. After the clay is rammed you bring the shooting needle out, and then you've got a hole going through the clay right into the black powder. So, you've brought down your black powder with you, you've also brought down some straws of wheat, or perhaps oat straw, then you'd try to fill up these hollow straws with very fine black powder, to make a fuse.

Once you'd got one of these hollow straws filled with gunpowder then you inserted it through the hole in the clay that you'd just made, and then packed it tightly round and then in the end of the straw, which is filled with gunpowder, you put in a little piece of brown paper, which has been soaked in saltpetre, and that gives you an additional fuse. So then you do all your eight or ten holes in a similar process and then it's time, the end of the shift, to fire these holes. So you gets towards late in the afternoon, and you get yourself ready for out, and then using the candle on your helmet, you set fire to all these slow matches on the fuses, and away you go. And as you're climbing up the ladders to go home, with a bit of luck you hear the charges going off and you know the next day you'll be able to come down and pick around and start enlarging the tunnel. Of course, that's the easy way out, with black powder, now that black powder was only introduced about 1670, but we've been mining for a thousand years or more before then, and what we used before then was to take fires down – lots and lots of combustibles, mostly wood and bones and stuff like that, and at the end of the working day you would stack all these combustibles against the rock face and set fire to it, and then you'd have to rush out before the smoke from the fire overcame you. In the lead mining we have a term which is 'mineral time', which means there's no mining takes place after four o'clock in the afternoon, because that's when everybody sets their fires, and it would be dangerous to stay underground because you might get overcome by the fumes. Next day if the rocks were still hot you'd throw a bit of water on it, on the rocks and that might help to crack the rocks - that's what we call fire setting. And another way which was very, very labour intensive was to make what modern pot-holers call a coffin level, and that is where a miner lays on his side using a gad, a wedge and he, with a short hammer, he strikes down the side of the passage way in beautiful sweeping strikes with, either the gad or a pick.

So after you've done your firing that's the last process of the day, because of the fumes so you climb back out up to daylight, it might have been a nice hot day, your field of hay's dried, so you have a rest by leading your hay at night into your little barn so that you can feed your cow right through the winter.

Drill bits could be sharpened on odd bits of gritstone you'd taken down the mine but after a while it might need tempering in the forge, so after many sharpenings you'd perhaps bring out your drill steels out of the mine and perhaps a village blacksmith would put a fresh temper on your drill steel. And Mr Barnes the blacksmith at Eyam used to travel round and he would sort out and re-temper your drill steels for you.

And if the mine is extended, and presumably there are other mines around also doing the same thing, how do you check where you are in the ground in relationship to the surface: make sure you are within your measured area and you're not crossing other's workings.

This was how lawyers got fat. There's hardly any way underground you could tell that you are not infringing by a few yards your neighbour's mine. And that's why there are so many disputes at the Barmote Court, because one miner would claim that his neighbour was coming in on his vein. Of course the Barmaster and his deputies would have to descend the mine and try and work it out, because a lot of this ended up in very expensive court cases.

Water was a terrible problem, because sometimes you didn't have enough on the surface for dressing your lead, and as I say you had to haul it up from underground in barrels to be able to dress your lead on the surface. And then of course in the later centuries when you've been mining at a certain site for four hundred years going deeper and deeper after a while you hit the saturation level in the ground, the water table. Thereafter, any deeper that you want to go after you've hit the water table, you have to pump it out. Oh, that was desperate. They used to try and haul it out onto the surface using the horse engine with barrels but that couldn't keep up really. You'd have several men in lifts working a rag and chain pump where you had a chain with leather balls attached to it into the chain and then it would go down into the flooded sump and as you wound it the chain came back up a pipe and these leather balls brought the water up like a piston in a cylinder, and men worked for hours underground winding the water out with the rag and chain pumps. But very, very difficult. One of the most favoured methods that were used in Derbyshire was to drive in a drainage sough, in places like Calver.

It was a very good idea to have two shafts at a mine, not only for safety in case one falls in but also for ventilation. Because when you are working at the fore-field you can quite easily use up the oxygen that is available there, and also the poisonous gas tends to form into puddles in the mine, and you can easily succumb to what they call choke damp.

It was a hard life but around here there wasn't a big choice of other jobs to go to.

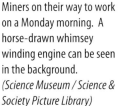

Miners on their way to work on a Monday morning. A horse-drawn whimsey winding engine can be seen in the background.
(Science Museum / Science & Society Picture Library)

12. The Last of the Hucklow Miners?

The modern Mill Dam Mine was designed to extract fluorspar, which is much in demand for the fluorochemical industry based in Runcorn.

In the modern mine the levels are 10 feet wide driveways and miners can actually drive underground from Hucklow to their workings. There is no crawling through narrow tunnels with only a candle on your Bradda hat to light the way, but conditions are not pleasant and there is still the water constantly dripping on you through the rock. Water is also used in the drilling process and helps to damp down the dust. Disposal of the water is still as much a problem as centuries ago but today there are electric pumps rather than horse driven gins or steam-powered engines by which it is pumped from drain sumps and into the very swallows the old lead miners used.

The ancient miners would not have had to contend with the noise and vibrations of powerful machinery, so loud that the modern miners have to wear ear protectors or fenders. The atmosphere can be just as unpleasant with the fumes from exhausts of the machinery and those resulting from the explosives used in the mine. To counteract this there is the constant noise and draught from the ventilation system whose fans have to be checked regularly.

The following piece is based on a recording of a conversation with Stephen Ollerenshaw of Rose Farm, Grindlow made in January 2008 – one time fluorspar miner with Glebe Mines at Mill Dam Mine in Great Hucklow and Sallet Hole at Stoney Middleton.

Stephen operating a drilling rig at Sallet Hole (Paul Deakin)

Get up in a morning, get dressed, have breakfast, go to work, go into the changing area, get undressed, then dressed into your mining clothes, go into the snap cabin, see the shift boss and he'd give you a report on how far they'd got on the previous shift and what was left to do. We would then be transported down the main heading in a Hilux jeep or a dumper truck and be dropped off at various places of work, some for heading work, some slit work, drilling or loading spar onto dumpers.

You'd go into your area and look for any danger, loose rocks, things like that, check it all over, check the machine and start the drilling process. The drilling is done in what's called a slit, which is a kind of side tunnel from the main heading tunnel, about 10ft high by 11ft wide. This runs parallel to the vein we're working on and is the roadway giving access to the working and also for taking out the minerals. The idea is to break up the vein with explosives placed in a series of drilled holes and the resulting broken rock and vein material is extracted through the slit. The void left in the vein after extraction is backfilled with unwanted material from the previously worked gallery above. While this extraction is going on the drilling team is working in the next slit, probably about 20 feet further along the heading.

The machine drills a hole into the rock with a series of 4ft lengths of steel drilling rods; as the drilling progresses a new length is clamped on to the previous one until the drill reaches the required length – sometimes to over 100ft. Water is pumped through the drilling rods into the hole as the drilling progresses; this not only keeps the drill rods cool but also washe s drillings back down the hole – by examining these the drill operator gets some idea as to what kind of material the drill head is passing through – limestone, barytes, fluorspar, or whatever.

Each of these drill holes could take up to a couple of hours to complete, provided there are no snags, and depending on the kind of rock face we're working on it might need between 20 and 40 holes to be drilled in a particular pattern.

After the drilling is complete each hole is then packed with the explosive charge. First of all a plastic tube is inserted into each drill hole; it comes in 100ft lengths – looks a bit like a water pipe – with measured markings so we know how far it's passed down the hole – then we insert a pill of explosive and the cordite firing cord, which looks a bit like washing line, right to the end of the tube. Once this is in place then the rest of the tube is filled with more pills of explosive, each one being blown along the tube by a blast of air from what's known as an air breach powered by a compressor. Each hole would take between 20 and 40 kilos of explosive, so with up to 40 drill holes to fill this can take a bit of time, and might involve up to a ton of explosive being inserted.

This whole process of setting up for blasting out a new piece of vein extraction takes about two weeks.

When all was ready you'd prime the firing circuit and retire round a couple of corners before setting the whole thing off, which as you can imagine went off with an hell of a bang, but also with a sudden blast of air. Sometimes people could hear it on the surface. Peter Webster always 'phoned us when he'd heard us doing a firing – his farm stands over the vein. It took about two weeks to clear the slit of material which had been blasted out, most of it being broken into lumps which were easy to handle after the force of the confined explosion.

Meal breaks had to be taken outside of the mine as we weren't allowed to take food down there for health and safety reasons.

Conditions could be difficult – you were stood in water all the time and of course there was always water running out of the drill holes and running on to you. We would get 'wet money' – extra money to our normal pay if we had to work for long in these sort of condition.

At the end of a shift you'd fight for a seat back on one of the wagons, report to the boss with all your readings and things, then get undressed and into the shower. Of course this is the time when there'd be all sorts of horseplay going off, some of which I can't possibly go into here. Typical sort of thing was that you'd get yourself dry, and when you put your pants on you'd find someone had sprayed them with 'Deep Heat', or something similar, which would give you an unexpected warm glow. Other little tricks might be like when you got home and took your socks off you'd find yourself with black feet – while you'd been working someone had turned them inside out and then rubbed them up and down inside a smokey exhaust pipe.

It wasn't all fun, of course – sometimes things could become tricky; working underground has all kinds of dangers, no matter how well prepared you are. On one shift me and a mate, Nigel Potter, were working on the upper gallery preparing to backfill rock into the worked vein below. There was something like a 20 foot capping above these working and we were drilling bore holes ready to blast the rock down into the worked void beneath. After we drilled each hole we lined it with the usual plastic pipe to keep it clear. Anyway, we'd just taken a break and come back to the site, and there were some creaking noises coming from the plastic pipes we'd put in. We started to drill another hole in the capping but instead of the 20 feet of rock we expected it only went in about 5 feet before it appeared to be through the thickness of rock. Clearly there'd been a fall-off of rock into the lower levels while we'd been in the snap cabin. Then we thought we'd better retreat a little bit as we could hear these pipes creaking more and more. Then the geologist came down to have a look; we'd just withdrawn the boom of the drilling machine from the slit and I was having a look at things; fortunately I had a harness on tied with a rope to the wall because the whole of the floor suddenly disappeared in front of us taking the roof support rings with it so that the shale above also began to collapse in, so we all started to run back down the heading, and there was a hell of a draught of wind as well. Never run so fast.

Even though we were working at a depth of about 600 feet, the collapse caused a hole to appear on the surface about 30 feet deep which swallowed a tree which had been growing on the spot.

There was another occasion when I was working on driving a heading and we were breaking through an area of rock which had slickensides in it – this is where there had been a slippage or fault in the geology of the rock and it makes the rock unstable. This particular fault happened to be parallel to the heading we were driving, and of course you can't see it. I was just doing what we call 'dressing down', knocking any bits of loose rock from the sides of the new section of heading, and I hit this bit of rock and the whole slab came away and was falling towards me. I just managed to fall back in time,

but not far enough as the top part of it fell on my foot. That was three months off. Yes, nasty stuff is slickensides as it can catch you unawares. The old miners were equally fearful of its unpredictable nature.

When I was working in Mill Dam Mine, most of the extraction took place at the far end of the workings, that is the section towards Ladywash Mine. The access for vehicles to the lower working areas was down a spiral roadway at that end of the top level, so it took the loaded wagons about an hour to get back to the surface at the Mill Dam entrance in Hucklow.

I did the job of a Senior Long Hole Driller there and at Sallet Hole for eleven years, but even if they do open up fluorspar production again at Mill Dam Mine, they will have to manage it without me. I've done all the work I ever want to do down a fluorspar mine.

Left, an example of 'slickensides', a wall of rock showing the scars as a result of geological movement. On the right, an example of the volume of water that miners might have to cope with – this an outfall of a drainage level at Ladywash mine on Eyam Edge.

Remnants of mining activity in Black Engine mine on Eyam Edge – a crushed kibble (a bucket-like metal container for carrying ore), and the slowly decomposing remains of ore tubs which would have run on a railed track between the working face and the dressing floor or winding shaft.

(Photographs by Paul Deakin)

13. A School View

Early in the project we invited Brian Woodall to take his impersonation and tales of "T'owd Mon" to the pupils of Great Hucklow Primary School.

We also organised a visit of a party of pupils to the Silence Mine site when the Bee Orchids were blooming at their best (photo opposite).

Dr John Barnatt showed another party around the excavated site at High Rake.

These two pages contain some of the responses of the children to these experiences.

We envisage that the school will continue having contact with the project in the future.

A Day in the Mine, by Alexander

I get up at half-past five in the morning and feed the pigs, then I go to the coe and pick up my tools. I climb down the stemples and have breakfast down the mine. I lie on my side for ages picking at the rock with my slitting pick. The only light I have is the candle on top of my Bradda hat. I keep picking at the rock for ages and ages when I hear a rumbling in the passage behind me. I look round and crawl a bit up the passage and find a branch tunnel colapsed leading off the one I'm working in. I go back to the end of the tunnel and work for anothetr hals hour before getting the twigs I have brought down and set fire to them against the face I'm working on. Hopefully it will make my job easier tomorrow. I go back up the tunnel. I have made two inches progress in my day's work. I go home and have some black pudding for tea then go to bed.

Silence Mine
One hundred years ago
Silence Mine was digging up lead
Lots of people going up and down
Lots of people milling around.
Now it stands silent
Still as stone
The ruin of a lead mine
A tribute of time.

By Lee

A Miner's Day
Going to the mine
With my hat from Bradda
Down the mine I go
Down the rusty ladder

I'm lying on my side
Using hammer and gad
Then someone comes,
It is my little lad.

I'm chiselling away at limestone
And I found some lead
I'm taking it to the coe
That's a miner's word for shed.

It's lunch time
Time for a well earned treat
Black pudding sandwiches
For me and my son to eat.

It's going very well
I'm loading the lead
Onto a very bumpy
Wooden sled.

My day has ended
I'm going home,
For I am very tired
From chipping stone.

by James, Ajax and Lawrence

ORCHID
Jamie

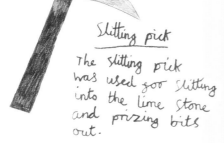

Slitting pick

The slitting pick
was used for slitting
into the lime stone
and prizing bits
out.

The Old Mine

The mine that had been working so long
Now collapsed, ruined and gone.
Down the mineshfts fathoms deep,
Water does now seep.
Out of the chimneys smoke used ro rise,
Out of their towering size,
They used to be so high and grand,
Now they lie in pieces on the ground.
The mine that had been working so long,
Now collapsed, ruined, and gone.

                                by Alexander

High Rake Mine

Up at High Rake mine
Chimneys used to stand
Really high and grand.
The engines began with a toot
Then someone called Henry Boot
Took it all down
To build houses in Bradda town.
Now it all that can be found
Lies on the ground.

                                by Shaun

Bradder hat

This hat was for
the miners to wear.
It had a candle on
the front which
was the only light
the miners had to
work by in the mine.

Gad

The miners put this
onto the rock and hit
it with a hammer
to prize into the stone.

14. Flora of the Hucklow Lead Rakes

Researched and written by Lesley Ayers and Gillian Beer

The Lead Rakes of Hucklow are important for the diversity of plant life arising from the variable soil compositions and habitats created by the mining of the underlying rocks. Lead rake soils can contain high amounts of lead, with smaller amounts of barium. These are heavy metals and give rise to very toxic soils which are very important ecologically as they support lead-loving plants such as the Spring Sandwort, a rare heavy-metal-tolerant plant, the Mountain Pansy and other lead-tolerant variants such as Bladder Campion and Wild Thyme. This area is of international importance for the Spring Sandwort or 'Leadwort' as it is known locally.

The plant drawings (from life) and mine maps featured in this section are the work of Eunice Jennings.

Spring Sandwort or Leadwort

Some of the typical lead rake plants found on the Hucklow lead mining sites:

Mountain Pansy	Cowslip	Milkwort
Common Whitlow Grass	Mouse Ear Hawkweed	Bladder Campion
Wild Thyme	Early Purple Orchid	Bee Orchid

Summer flowers at Silence Mine Site

Landscape

This section reflects on

    how the geology of the land is important in determining the acidic, neutral or lime nature of the soil

    how the mining activity has disturbed the soil and habitat over a period of time

    how the land, now in different stages of regeneration, supports different plant communities.

Great Hucklow lies within a typical upland Peak District landscape of dry stone walls enclosing fields about 300m above sea level. The landscape and habitats have been determined by the underlying rocks: the Limestone plateau of the White Peak and Millstone and Shale Grits of the Dark Peak. The Grit Stone gives an acidic nature to the soil which is often waterlogged and supports acid-loving plants, such as Gorse, Wood Sage, and Heather. The Limestone gives rise to a shallow, well drained soil, rich in nutrients and lime, which supports calcareous plants, such as Mouse Ear Hawkweed and Wild Thyme.

Gritstone Edge

Spoil Heaps

The Great Hucklow lead vein crosses the boundary of the Limestone plateau and the Grit Stone. The boundary is roughly defined by the steeply sloping Grit stone edge meeting the flatter Limestone plateau. The lead veins are primarily in the Monsal limestone (see diagram below). To the east of Windmill, the Monsal limestone, with associated lead, dips under the Eyam limestone. This in turn dips under the Millstone Grit and then the Shale Grit. Mining along the lead vein has raised the limestone with its minerals to the surface. In some areas these 'polluted' metal and mineral rich spoil heaps support specialised communities of plants which are specially adapted to tolerate the high lead content of the soil. Where the mine shafts were on the Grit Stone, as at Silence Mine and Have-At-All, the spoil heaps are of variable soil composition whilst the undisturbed area around the mines is acidic.

Stone Stile

Geology Map of the Hucklow Vein

Scrub

Dry Stone Walls

Open cast working has been practisedfor many hundreds of years. The miners worked along the lead vein to extract the mineral they wanted and left the unwanted rocks, soil and minerals behind in small spoil heaps around the shafts they dug. These characteristic hills and dips are in evidence along the approach to High Rake Mine from Great Hucklow and to a lesser extent at Silence Mine.

In the last 150 years deeper shafts have been dug to extract ore from greater depths: hence the need for buildings to house engines and crush the stone. There are now ruined buildings and larger deposits left around the shafts. At Windmill, open cast mining created a large quarry which has since been filled in.

In more recent times the residual waste heaps have been reworked to extract fluorspar and baryte, and the hillocks have been flattened for agriculture or used as dumping areas. Heavily grazed areas do not support a wide diversity of plants, but where the animals have been controlled, as is the case on the lead rakes, plant communities thrive. Where the land has not been used for agriculture such as in the woodland or along the Grit Stone edge, the vegetation is beginning to mature.

Spoil Heaps

Recent excavations

Now, the lead rakes show a variety of phases in the regeneration of the land:

Newly excavated soil from archaeological activity.

Sparse grassland – where the soil is still mineral rich and humus poor: here smaller 'lead-loving' or 'poor-soil-loving' plants can survive without competition from the tall vegetation. These areas, at High Rake, Have-it-All and the Washing Plant, are where the nationally rare lead tolerant-plants are found.

Hay meadow type grassland – where the soil is becoming less poor through the breakdown of old plants: on this ungrazed grassland taller species can compete with the tussocky grasses. These areas are adjacent to the sparse grassland areas and also at Silence Mine. They support a wide number of plants.

Scrub – of Hazel and Hawthorn. On the ungrazed slopes this is beginning to destroy the conditions for the smaller flowering plants.

Woodland at Silence Mine

Woodland – where trees have been planted in some places to prevent animals from grazing on the lead polluted grass or the naturally-occurring ash woods. The woodland fringes are at their best in spring and early summer before the leaf canopy blocks out the light.

Sparse Grassland

Wetland

Wild Flowers

Bee Orchid

There are several important areas of botanical interest along the Great Hucklow Lead rakes. These are the High Rake Mine, Have-At-All Shaft, Silence Mine and the Washing Plant areas. High Rake, Have-it-All and the Washing Plant are important for their lead-rich spoil heaps and the profusion of Spring Sandwort, a nationally rare plant. Yellow Mountain Pansies which are also tolerant of lead soils grow just below the Washing Plant. Silence Mine is important for the variety of orchids, namely the Bee, Early Purple, Common Spotted, Southern Marsh and Fragrant Orchids.

Each of these areas is now discussed in more detail and flower plans provided for High Rake, Have-it-All and Silence Mine at the end of this section. In these the flowers are listed in flowering order.

High Rake is on the limestone and provides a lead-rich spoil and sparse grassland habitat around the central area close to the excavations where Spring Sandwort, Hairy Whitlow Grass, Fairy Flax, Wild Thyme, Hairy Rockcress and Eyebright grow. There is a slightly richer calcareous hay meadow grassland habitat in the outer areas where the taller plants such as Knapweed and Meadow Saxifrage can survive. Recent excavations have provided a new spoil for sandy, lead-tolerant plant populations to thrive. High Rake is in a very exposed position with prevailing winds sweeping across the hillocks during the winter months. However, of all the areas in Great Hucklow this provides the most diverse of plant populations and from April onwards provides a wide variety of wild flowers.

Have At All shaft area is a south-facing sheltered slope surrounded by woodland. The grassland below the Have At All shaft is a mixture of sparse grassland and hay meadow type grassland. The overlying Shales have been disturbed by lead workings and the underlying limestone and mineral have been brought to the surface. Early in the year the ground is clear and there is a profusion of Spring Sandwort and Milkwort growing here. The slope becomes overgrown in places towards the summer. Wild Thyme, possibly a lead-tolerant variant, is prominent in early summer. Fairy Flax and Hairy Rock Cress can be found in the sparse sandy areas.

Harebell

Field Scabious

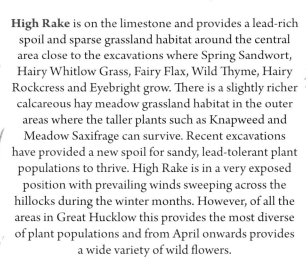

Bluebell

Cowslip

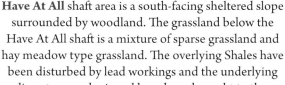

Knapweed

Mountain Pansy

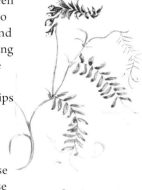

Tufted Vetch

The majority of the woodland around the area has been subject to disturbance from the lead workings and so does not support a Bluebell population. The woodland is also densely shaded in the summer and few flowering plants can survive under the tree canopy. There are Bluebells to be seen in the undisturbed woodland fringes, along with Common Dog-Violets and Cowslips in spring.

The verge on the road up to the Gliding Club is particularly interesting: it lies on the edge of the workings. Species on the uphill side are acidic (Gorse and Wood Sage), whereas calcareous species (Mouse Ear Hawkweed) are found on downhill verge.

Silence Mine is on a sheltered south-facing slope. There are no sparse grassland areas at Silence Mine so Spring Sandwort is not found here. In the clearings between the scrub and woods there is a hay meadow type grassland on neutral-to-lime soil arising from the mining activity. Here Cowslips flourish early in the year, followed by an display of Orchids. Field Scabious, Knapweed and Meadow Cranesbill attract a variety of butterflies later in year. Bladder Campion, possibly a lead-tolerant variant, can also be found at Silence Mine.

Meadow
Cranesbill

In the woodland fringes close to the ruined buildings Red Campion and Sweet Cicely grow in abundance before the dense canopy shades the area in summer. The path leading down to the grassland area is fringed with Common Dog-Violets in spring, then Tormentil and Bugle later on.

Foxglove

To the furthest east beyond the boundary of Silence mine site the slope is becoming over-run by bracken. Here acidic loving plants such as Foxglove and Tormentil are found at the top of the slope, with the lime/neutral plants growing lower down the slope where the land has been disturbed.

Early Purple
Orchid

Yellow Rattle

The Washing Plant lies on a south-west-facing slope on the Grit Stone. The mound and field below the washing plant contain soil rich in metal and minerals: the waste from the washing process. Early in the year Common Whitlow Grass flowers, then later in April and May, Common Dog Violets, Mountain Pansies, Spring Sandwort, Hairy Bittercress, Milkwort, and Tormentil can be seen. Unusually, Wood Anemone carpets the field giving a wonderful display in early summer.

Red Campion

Moon Penny and
Red Clover

Lords and Ladies

Spear Thistle

Spring Sandwort

Common
Dog Violet

Herb Robert

Honeysuckle

Wild Strawberry

Have-At-All

Woodland fringes
Common Dog-Violet, Germander Speedwell, Ground Ivy, Pignut, Wild Strawberry, Water Avens, Bluebell, Crosswort, Cuckoo Flower, Lesser Stitchwort, Red Campion, Meadow Cranesbill

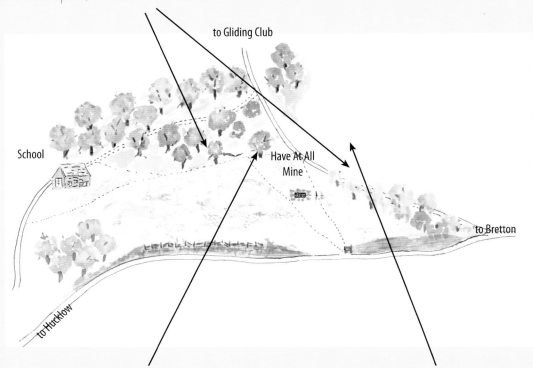

to Gliding Club

School

Have At All Mine

to Bretton

to Hucklow

Road Verge (edge of Shale Grit)
Common Dog-Violets, Ground Ivy, Wild Strawberry, Woodsage, Crosswort, Bluebell, Greater Stitchwort,
Gorse, Goatsbeard, Meadow Cranesbill,
Bladder Campion, Mouse-ear Hawkweed, Dotted Loosestrife, Hedge Woundwort, Knapweed,
Rosebay Willowherb, Foxglove, Wood Avens.

Grassland on Shales disturbed by lead workings
Cowslip, Germander Speedwell, Spring Sandwort, Common Milkwort, Crosswort, Meadow Buttercup, Hairy Rock Cress, Bush Vetch, Birds Foot Trefoil, Wild Thyme, Lady's Bedstraw,
Red Clover, Fairy Flax, Bladder Campion, Rough Hawkbit, Eyebright, Knapweed, Field Scabious, Harebell

Silence Mine

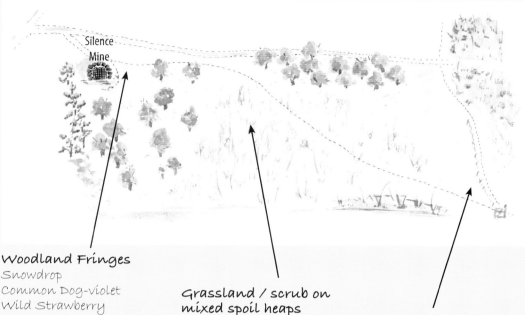

Silence
Mine

Woodland Fringes

Snowdrop
Common Dog-violet
Wild Strawberry
Red Campion
Crosswort
Ground Ivy
Bluebell
Sweet Cicely
Welsh Poppy
Bush Vetch
Germander Speedwell
Bugle
Tormentil

Grassland / scrub on mixed spoil heaps

Coltsfoot, Cowslip,
Crosswort, Early Purple
Orchid, Red Campion,
Cuckoo Flower, Red Clover,
Lady's Bedstraw,
Germander Speedwell,
Mouse-Ear Hawkweed,
Birds Foot Trefoil, Milkwort
(white),
Common Spotted Orchid
(including variant
Albiflora), Fairy Flax,
Bladder Campion, Ox-Eye
Daisy,
Southern Marsh Orchid
and variants, Bee Orchid,
Fragrant Orchid, Tufted
Vetch, Field Scabious,
Knapweed,
Hay Rattle, Goatsbeard,
Eyebright, Harebell,
Meadow Cranesbill,
Agrimony.

Grassland/scrub on shales

Cowslip
Wild Pansy
Tormentil
Pignut
Red and White Campion
Slender St Johns Wort
Foxglove
Tufted Vetch
Bracken
Hoary Plantain
Eyebright
Harebell

High Rake

Flowers common to all High Rake Areas

Coltsfoot, Ground Ivy, Lesser Celandine, Bulbous Buttercup, Bush Vetch, Crosswort, Cuckoo Flower, Forget-me-not, Germander Speedwell. Glaucus Sedge, Lady's Mantle, Meadow Buttercup, Meadow Saxifrage, Red Campiom, Bladder Campion*, Common Comfrey, Common Gigwort, Dame's Violet, Dog Rose, Dotted Loosestrife, Hawkweed, Hedge Woundwort, Male Fern, Meadow Cranesbill, Meadow Vetchling, Mpuse-ear Hawkweed, Ox-eye Daisy, Pignut, Quaking Grass, Red Clover, Rough Hawkbit, Salad Burnet, Yellow Rattle, Common Knapweed, Field Scabious, Harebell*, Lady's Bedstraw, Small Scabious, Snowberry, Spear Thistle, Tufted Vetch, Golden Rod

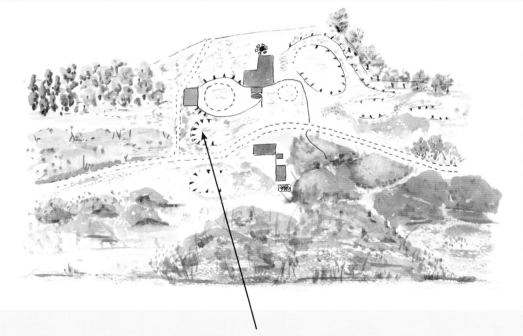

Sparse Grassland and Hay-meadow type Grassland

Common Whitlow Grass, Cowslip, Hairy Bittercress, Bird's Foot Trefoil*, Spring Sandwort*, Pignut, Common Milkwort, Hairy Rock Cress, Salad Burnet, limestone Bedstraw, Hoary Whitlow Grass, Bird's Foot Trefoil, Rough Hawkbit, Salad Burnet, Fragrant Orchid*, Fairy Flax, Wild Thyme*, Eyebright*, Harebell*

* Plants known to be lead-tolerant

The photographs on the following pages are of plants found on the local lead rakes. Most of the photgraphs of the plants have been taken in situ by people engaged in the study.

Goatsbeard

Lady's Bedstraw

Hoary Whitlow Grass

A Fritillary butterfly on Knapweed

Agrimony

Bee Orchid

Bitter Vetchling

Bugle

Bush Vetch

Common Spotted Albiflora Orchid

Common Spotted Orchid

Cowslip

Crosswort

Bladder Campion

Bluebell

Coltsfoot

Common Dog Violet

Common Whitlow Grass

Dog Rose

Eyebright

Fairy Flax

Cuckoo Flower

Early Purple Orchid

Yellow Rattle

Wild Blue Pansy

Fragrant Orchid

Goatsbeard

Greater Stitchwort

Hoary Plantain

Hairy Rock Cress

Harebell

Heath Bedstraw

Herb Robert

Knapweed

Yarrow

Red Campion

Red Clover

Snowdrops

Meadow Saxifrage

Common Milkwort (White)

Common Milkwort (Blue)

Mountain Pansy

Pignut

Field Scabious

Southern Marsh Orchid

Tormentil

Water Avens

Germander Speedwell

Spring Sandwort – 'Leadwort'

Sweet Cicely

Thistle

Tufted Vetch

Wild Thyme

Wood Anemone

Wood Anemone group at Washing Plant

15. GLOSSARY

A selection of words and terms used by miners in the Derbyshire orefield. Again we would express grateful thanks to Dr JH Rieuwerts for allowing us to use material from his book, *A Glossary of Derbyshire Lead Mining Terms* (PDMHS, 1998)

ADIT – a horizontal tunnel into a hillside, often called a level, and sometimes functioning as a sough.

ADVENTURERS – investors or shareholders in a mine or sough.

AGENT – the representative of the mine owner or the adventurers; usually concerned with the day–to–day management of the mine.

ARREST – proceeding by which the working of a mine is stopped.

Barmaster – the representative of the Crown, or the Crown lessee, responsible for the administration of mining law and courts, measuring ore and measuring out meers along the length of a vein. Deputy Barmasters were often appointed when the amount of mining required it.

BARMOTE (or BARMOOT) – the lead miners' court of law, originally held twice a year in each liberty, but now only once a year. The jury was once 24 in number but now 12, charged with judicial duties continuously from one court to the next. The jury is called 'The Body of the Mine'. The biannual (annual) courts were sometimes called Great Barmotes, whilst lesser disputes could be settled by ad hoc Small Barmotes.

BARYTE (formerly barytes) – the mineral barium sulphate (BaSO); commonly called cawk, caulk, calk or heavy spar.

BELLAND – finely powdered lead ore, usually as in mine waste. Poisonous if ingested by animals or humans. Animals grazing on meadows contaminated with belland are said to be 'bellanded'. A belland yard is a walled enclosure to prevent stock trying to graze on the mine waste.

BING – large pieces or ore drawn from the mine and requiring little further processing.

BLENDE – another name for zinc sulphide.

BODY OF THE MINE – another more common name for the Grand Jury – miners, having a perfect knowledge of the mining customs.

BOLE – a primitive type of smelting hearth, usually sited on hilltops, hence the frequent place name Bole Hill.

BOOTHERS – rock boulders found associated wih the stratas of Eyam imestone.

BOUSE – lead ore as raised from the mine before dressing.

BROWN-HENNS – a base mineral found in veins mixed with the lead ore ; it is, with calk and other substances, a component of the deads or rubbish rejected by miners.

BUCKER or BUCKING IRON – a broad, flat-headed hammer used mainly by women to break up the ore to separate it from the gangue minerals.

BUDDLE – a wooden or stone trough or series of troughs used to wash light minerals away from the lead ore particles trapped by baffles. 'To buddle' is to use a buddle.

CALCITE – the mineral calcium carbonate (CaCO); sometimes worked as calc–spar for decorative purposes.

CALK, CAULK, CAWK – baryte (see above); the chief source of barium chemicals in industry; also widely used as barite mud in oil–well drilling.

CAT DIRT – decomposed toadstone; weathered basalt lava.

CAVERS – poor people, often old women, who scavenged and reworked hillocks for discarded ore. Also applied to those persons who go about the mines to beg or steal ore from the miner's coes.

CHANNEL – weathered toadstone.

CHEEKS – the walls or sides of a vein.

CLIMBING SHAFT – a narrow shaft specifically for access into the mine. Usually fitted with stemples to act as rungs in a ladder.

COE – a small building or shed, usually of stone, over or near a mine, in which the miners kept their tools and a change of clothing. The climbing shaft was sometimes under a trapdoor in the floor of the coe.

COMPOSITION – money paid to sough drivers in reward for profits from lead ore rendered accessible.

COPE – a duty originally paid by the miners, later by the smelter, to the Lord to allow them to sell their ore to whoever they wish. Usually a fixed price per load.

COPER – a man or gang of men who mined lead on the cope bargain system.

CORFE or CORVE – a crude wooden sledge used to convey ore etc. underground, sometimes along a wooden plankway.

CROSS-CUT – a passage driven through solid rock from one vein to another.

CUPOLA – a reverberatory furnace for smelting ore.

DEADS – waste rocks from mine workings usually stacked in abandoned stopes, sometimes on timber platforms which are now unstable.

DIAL – a miners' compass used in surveying underground.

DIP – the inclination of strata.

DISH – a measure for lead ore, either oblong or circular. It varied between liberties but was usually about 14 or 15 Winchester pints capacity. Nine dishes make one load; about $3^3/_4$ loads make one ton. One dish is about 65 Ibs. A standard dish made in 1513 is kept in the Moot Hall at Wirksworth.

EGG AND EYE – the notch and slot made in opposite walls of a vein to hold a stemple or wooden beam.

ENGINE – any winding or pumping machinery whether worked by hand, horse, steam or water–power.

ENGINE SHAFT – a larger shaft equipped with winding or pumping machinery instead of a stowes.

FANGS – wood or metal pipes used to convey fresh air to the workings.

FATHOM – a measure of six feet, commonly used to express depths of mines or shafts.

FAULT – a geological term denoting the fracture and displacement of strata.

FIRING or FIRE-SETTING – the practice before the days of explosives of lighting a fire against the face of the vein to open cracks and thus to ease the extraction of rock. Fire–setting could only be done after 4 p.m. and before 8 a.m.

FISSURE – a crack or joint in the rocks, either open or filled with loose stones.

FLAT – a body of ore generally lying more or less horizontal with equal length and width, often parallel to the local stratification. By elongation flats graded into pipes.

FLUORSPAR – the mineral fluorite $(CaF-)$; a common constituent of the Derbyshire mineral veins. Widely used as a flux for fluidizing slag in furnaces, as a source of fluorine in chemical industry, in ceramics and special glasses. Clear, white, yellow, pink and blue varieties occur as well as the banded Blue John at Castleton.

FOREFIELD – the active working face in the mine, usually the furthest point from the shaft.

FOTHER or FODDER – a measure of lead metal used by the merchants, varying from liberty to liberty and between markets and ports. Ranges from 1680 to 2520 Ibs usually nearer the latter.

FOUNDER – the first miner to work a mine, or the first meers allocated by the Barmaster, or the first shaft sunk on a vein.

FREEING – the act of delivering to the Barmaster a dish of ore to establish ownership of a new vein or mine.

GALENA– the mineral lead sulphide (PbS); the chief ore of lead.

GANG or GANGUE – the minerals found with the lead ore, generally regarded as waste. Fluorspar and baryte may be more valuable nowadays and many hillocks have been re–processed for them.

GATE – a way or passage in a mine, an access route.

GIN – a winding engine; often driven by horses, also known as a whim.

GIN CIRCLE – the circular track around which the horse(s) walked to work the gin.

GINGING – the dressed stonework around the shaft holding the loose ground near the surface.

GRAVEL ORE – loose lumps of ore, found in shacks or self–opens.

GROVE or GROOVE – a mine; sometimes applied to a length of vein being worked as a single mine; occasionally restricted to open workings at the surface.

HADE – the slope of a vein from the vertical.

HEADING – alternative name for a gate, cross–cut or adit.

HILLOCKS – old waste heaps.

HILLOCKING – re–working waste for unrecovered minerals.

ICLES – stalactites, as in caves (also called Watricle or Water–icicles).

JAGGER – one who carried lead ore from the mine to the smelter on mules or horses.

JIG – a box–like device used to separate lead ore from gangue minerals by shaking them up and down on a sieve in water.

JURY or GRAND JURY – the jury of the Barmote Court, once 24 but now 12 in number, drawn from amongst working miners.

KIBBLE or KEBBLE – a large bucket used to raise ore up a shaft.

LEVEL – a horizontal tunnel, adit, sough or gate. A level may also be a surveying instrument.

LIBERTY – the district in which the miner searches for lead ore. Derbyshire has possibly 50 liberties with slightly varying laws and customs. Some are Crown liberties (via the Duchy of Lancaster), other Crown liberties are leased to the Dukes of Devonshire and Rutland. Several smaller liberties are privately owned.

LOAD – a measure of lead ore, being 9 dishes, about $3^3/_4$ loads to the ton.

LORD – the owner of the mineral liberty (sometimes as a lessee or farmer from the Crown). The Lord received the Lot and Cope and freeing dishes.

LORD'S MEER – a length of vein laid out by the Barmaster for the Lord, who receives all the ore mined from it, or who makes special arrangements with the miners.

LOT – the share of ore due to the Lord, usually every 13th dish, though he might take anything from a 10th to a 25th according to the Liberty or according to the difficulty of extracting the ore.

MEER – a measure of the length of a vein, varying in different Liberties: 27, 28, 29, or 32 yards. Two founder meers are allocated to the finder of a new vein. The Lords's Meer followed and then taker meers were added as required.

NICKING – failure to work a mine may result in another miner claiming it by asking the Barmaster to 'nick' the stowes, i.e. to cut a piece of wood out. Three nickings allow the mine to be handed over to the claimant, unless work has been obstructed by water or lack of ventilation.

OFFAL – waste, gangue and rock, sometimes including unrecoverable lead ore.

OLD MAN or T'Owd Mon – places worked by former miners, or the former miners themselves.

OPEN – sometimes Self–open – a naturally open cavern or fissure.

ORE – the valuable mineral from which metal may be extracted. In Derbyshire this refers to lead ore.

PEE – the point of intersection at which two veins meet and cross one another at an angle

PIG or PIG O'LEAD – a block or ingot of lead metal cast at the smelter's works. Commonly 8 pigs make one fodder.

PIPE or PIPE VEIN – a body of ore and other minerals lying more or less horizontally but longer than wide. Many pipes are infillings or linings of pre–existing caverns. Pipes may branch out of rakes.

QUARTER CORD – ground allowed to the miner either side of his vein to deposit his waste and build his coe. Usually a quarter of a meer in width.

RAG AND CHAIN – primitive pumps which raised water by wads of rags wedged in a chain wound through hollowed out tree–trunks.

RAKE – the main type of mineral vein – a body of ore and gangue disposed more or less vertically and running across country for a mile or more. The boundary between a rake and the smaller scrin is not clearly definable.

RANGE OR RANDOM – the expected direction and extent of a vein beyond current workings.

RIDER – a mass of rock dividing a vein. Also called a horse.

RISE – an underground shaft driven upwards above a working.

SCRIN – a short vertical mineral vein. Of no great width not normally more than a few hundred metres long. Often branching out of a rake, sometimes in groups or 'swarms'.

SELF-OPEN – a large natural cavern.

SHACK – a natural opening in the ground, either

at the surface or underground; often filled with loose rocks. Sometimes known as a shake or shake–hole.

SHALE-GATE – a tunnel driven through shale.

SINKERS – men who make shafts.

SLAG – the waste material produced in smelting ore. Sometimes re–processed to recover more metal at a later date.

SLICKENSIDES – the grooved surface produced by the movement of strata along faults. Sometimes with shiny surfaces on galena, and sometimes in a state of stress and liable to explode on being disturbed by mining. Explosive slickensides is sometimes known as cracking–whole.

SMELTING – the process whereby metal is extracted from ore.

SMITHAM – finely ground ore produced during crushing.

SOLE – the floor of a mine or sough; the lowest level worked.

SOUGH – an adit or level specifically driven to drain a mine or mines.

SOUGHERS – men who excavate soughs.

SOUGH MASTERS – investors who finance the driving of soughs.

SPAR – a collective term for minerals accompanying the lead ore; includes fluorspar, baryte (heavy spar), and calcite (calcspar).

STEMPLE – a piece of wood wedged across a vein or stopeto provide a rung in a ladder; sometimes part of a platform for disposal of deads or for roof support. Dressed stone stemples occur in a few mines.

STEWARD – the presiding officer at the Barmote Court; the Lord's executive officer.

STOPE – the cavity left after working out a vein.

STOWES, STOCE, STOES – the wooden windlass over a shaft for raising ore. Though a single item, stowes were usually referred to as a pair. Stowes had to be made to a definite pattern without nails. The existence of a stowes on a mine was proof of ownership.

STRIKE – the course or direction of the strata or of a vein.

SUMP – an internal shaft, not connected to the surface; may be called a winze or a turn. A sump may also be a hollow in the bottom of a mine

where water collects before pumping out.

SWALLOW or SWALLET – a natural opening which takes water away. May also refer to a hole on the surface where a stream goes underground.

TAILINGS – the finely ground waste from mineral processing.

TITHE – from ancient time 1/10th of all lead ore raised. Later this 'duty' passed into the hands of proprietors appointed by the Crown.

TOADSTONE – a collective term for volcanic basalt of several types; it may be massive, columnar, vesicles (with gas bubbles); it may be altered to a green clay or it may be a volcanic fragmental rock known as tuff.

TURN – an underground shaft, also called a sump or winze. Several turns in a climbing shaft may be alongside a single engine shaft.

TURNTREE – an alternative name for a stowes.

THE TWENTY-FOUR – the Grand Jury of the Barmote Court, the 'Body of the Mine'; later reduced to twelve.

VEIN – a body of minerals enclosed by rock.

VEIN-STUFF – the minerals in a vein.

WATER-GATE – a drainage level or sough.

WATER-ICICLES or WATRICLES – stalactites.

WAYBOARD – a clay bed between limestone beds, usually not more than a few inches thick; often a volcanic dust layer and greenish in colour.

WHEAT ORE or WHITE ORE – lead carbonate (cerussite PbCO). Occasionally worked as a lead ore: once used in paint manufacture.

WHIM – a winding engine, worked by horses or steam.

WHIMSEY – a horse or steam–driven winding engine.

WINZE – an underground shaft connecting one level with another.

WISKET – a small wooden basket, often carried by boys, used for transporting ore, or waste rock from the forefield to a haulage shaft.

WOUGHS – the limestone walls or of a vein.

16. Acknowledgements and Sources

Published by : *Hucklow Publishing for Great Hucklow and District Community Spirit Committee*
Project Manager : *Patricia Miles*
Art Work, Design and Layout : *Peter Miles*
Writers and Contributers : *Patricia Miles, Peter Miles, Sheila Martin, John Barnatt, Tony Greenfield, Liz Greenfield, Lesley Ayres, Gillian Beer, Andrew Bower, John Elkins*
Editorial Advice : *Tony Greenfield and Colin Greenland*

We are extremely grateful to:

The Heritage Lottery Fund for awarding the grant to enable us to produce the book and its officers for their understanding and encouragement.

Great Hucklow Community Spirit Committee for its support and encouragement in applying for the grant and fulfilling its requirements.

We would like to thank the following who have given us invaluable help and encouragement:

Dr John Barnatt, senior research archaeologist, Peak District National Park Authority, for writing the article on High Rake Mine and his helpful advice.

Dr J H Rieuwerts for overseeing much of our research and giving us the benefit of his extensive knowledge

The late Nellie Kirkham whose article on the Great Hucklow Mines published by PDHMS first inspired us to produce the book.

Dr John Beck and Doug Nash for generously giving us a copy of their collected papers and research which will be included in the archive we are assembling for the parish, and for answering our many queries.

Michael Shuttleworth for making copies of his family papers available to us.

Members of PDHMS: Chris Heathcote and all those who have excavated High Rake and Silence Mines.

Brian Woodall – for taking his portrayal of T'Owd Mon to the children of Hucklow School and allowing us to record an interview with him.

John Elkins for giving us the information about the modern Mill Dam Mine.

East Midlands Oral History Archive for help in compiling our oral history archive.

The PDNPA Vision Project, especially Rebekah Newman and Louise Valantine.

We would also like to thank the many members of the Parish who have contributed or helped in so many ways, and in particular

Sheila Martin for researching the Little Hucklow Liberty so thoroughly, and Bob Campbell for his help and support.

Leslie Ayers and Gillian Beer for their research into the Flora of The Lead Rakes.

Eunice Jennings for her beautiful paintings of the flora.

Tony Greenfield for his care and time in editing some of the chapters.

Liz Greenfield for heading the team researching the Life of the Miners.

Andrew Bower for his assiduous research into the Liberty of Grindlow and various genealogies.

Stephen Ollerenshaw for his account of modern mining.

Kenneth Waterhouse, Tom Parkes and John Holmes for information about their families' histories.

Jack Binks for his informative tour of the Lead Rakes of the parish.

Christine Bucknell and Alan Jones for their research into the Life of the Miners.

Hester Messom, for time given in proof-reading.

Hannah Watson for her transcription services.

Great Hucklow Primary School – its teachers and the pupils for their poems and drawings.

Colin Greenland (honary member of the Parish)for sound editorial advice.

Manuscript sources

The sources of our information are not always included under each section, although they will be included in the archive we are compiling for the parish.

We have used material from the following archives and would like to thank all the archivists for their help, especially Stuart Band (Devonshire Collection) and John Goodchild (Goodchild collection).

Derbyshire Record Office, Matlock (DRO)

Sheffield Archives, Bagshawe Collection and Fairbank collection.

Chatsworth House, Devonshire Collection by kind permission of His Grace the Duke of Devonshire.

John Rylands Library Manchester (Bagshawe Collection).

Rieuwerts private collection.

Shuttleworth private papers, Nether Hall, Hathersage.

Goodchild collection, Wakefield.

John Beck and Doug Nash private collection, Eyam University of Nottingham Archive: Portland collection.

National Army Museum London: Letters of Robert Bagshaw.

Cumbria Record office: Le Fleming MSS.

Derbyshire Record Office: Letters to Quarter Sessions.

National army museum London: Letters of Robert Bagshaw.

Gravestones, St Peter's Church, Hope.

Tideswell Library , Copy of Parson Brown Diaries: 1792-9: Private Deeds.

The Census Returns and White's and Kelly's Directories.

Bibliography: Books and Articles

Barnatt John& Penny Rebecca, *The Lead Legacy*, pub. Peak District National Park Authority (2004).

Cameron K, *Place names of Derbyshire Part 1* Cambridge University Press Vol.XXVII.

Cox, *Derbyshire Churches Vol. 2* (1875)

Dias Jill, *Lead, Society and Politics in Derbyshire before The Civil War*, Midland History (1981).

Flindall Roger, *Calendar of the Barmasters' Derbyshire Lead Mining Records belonging to the Duchy of Lancaster, kept at Chatsworth House.*

Produced by Lynn Willies for PDHMS.

Ford T D and Rieuwerts JH, *Lead Mining in the Peak District*, Landmark publishing for PDHMS (2000).

FSC Publications, *Guide to Grassland Plants; Guide toWoodland Plants.*

Gaydon AT, *Victoria County History of Shropshire Vol.2* (1973).

Hopkinson GG, *Lead Mining in the Eyam District in the Eighteenth Century*, Derbyshire Archaeological Journal LXXX (1960).

Kiernan David, *The Derbyshire Lead Industry in the 16th Century*, Derbyshire Record Society 14 (Chesterfield 1989).

Kirkham Nellie, *Derbyshire lead Mining through the Centuries*, Pub. Bradford Barton Ltd. (1968).

Newton R., *Two Bagshaw Genealogies* (unpublished).

Philips Roger, *Wild Flowers of Britain.*

Porter William- Smith, *Notes from a Peakland Parish*, Republished 2000 Country books.

Rieuwerts J. H., *Derbyshire's Old Lead Mines and Miners*, Moreland Publishing Company (1972).
A History of the Laws and Customs of the Derbyshire Lead Mines.
Glossary of Derbyshire Lead Mining Terms, PDHMS (1998).
Lead Mining in Derbyshire, History, Development and Drainage-vol.1Castleton to the River Wye, Landmark Collectors' Library (2007).

Rose Francis, *The Wild Flowers Key.*

Sidney Richard &Fitter Richmond, *Wild Flowers of Britain and Northern Europe* Collins Pocket Guide Series.

Tapping Thomas, *A Treatise on the High Peak Mineral Customs and Mineral Acts 1851.*

ed. Una Rees, *The Cartulary of Lilleshall Abbey*, Shropshire Archaeological and Historical Society (1997).

Thompson RA, *An addition to the Derbyshire Series of Seventeen Century Tokens*, Numismatic Circular Sept 1992 pub. Spink.

Willies Lynn, *Lead and Lead Mining*, Shire Publications (1982).

Wood Andy ,*The Politics of Social Conflict: The Peak District 1520-1770*, Cambridge University Press (1999).

Articles published in the Bulletins of the Peak District Historical Mines Society

Kirkham Nellie , Great Hucklow Mines, Vol. 2 part 1 (May 1963).

Stokes Arthur H, Lead and Lead mining in Derbyshire: Special publication No. 2 (1996).

Critchley M F, A Survey of Little Mill Dam Mine, Great Hucklow Vol. 6 No2 (1977).

Rieuwerts JH, Back o' Th' Edge Mine Vol.12 No5 (1995).

Nash D A ,The Liberties of Grindlow and Foolow Vol. 6 No.6 (1977).

Willies Lynn, The Barker family and Wyatt Lead Mining Businesses 1730-1875 Vol.8 No.6 (1983).

Willies L, Rieuwerts JH, Flindall R, Wind Water and Steam Engines on Derbyshire Lead Mines Vol.7 No. 3 (1979).

Lawson J, Index to the Mining records in the Bagshawe Collection in the John Rylands Library, Manchester, parts 1-3 Vol. 3 (1968) Vol.4 (1969)

Maps

The maps of the Liberties and mine sites in the text have been adapted from various editions of the Ordnance Survey maps of the area, which we have the kind permission of Ordnance Survey to use.

Web Sites used in research

Genealogy website: Scott County Illinois

www. Plant-identification.co.uk/skye/

www.botanicalkeys.uk/flora/content/Search.Asp.

web.onetel.com/~imiller1/bagshaw.htm

www.genuki.org.uk/big/eng/DBY/GreatHucklow/index.html

www.andrewspages.dial.pipex.com/dby/kelly/hucklow.htm

freepages.genealogy.rootsweb.ancestry.com/~glossopfamily/census.htm#places

bcra.org.uk/pub/search/aut_pd1.htm#top

www.pdmhs.com/default.asp

www.ancestry.co.uk/

Photographs and Graphics

We would like to thank the following for their kind permission to use photographs and other graphics:

Paul Deakin, JH Rieuwerts, Michael Shuttleworth, John Barnatt, William Ayres, Sheffield Archives, Science Museum / Science & Society Picture Library, Derbyshire Local Studies Library, Peak District National Park Authority.

Eunice Jennings, who created the maps and plant drawings in the Flora section.

Peter Miles, who produced most of the photographs of the local sites and processed all the graphics included in the book.

18th Century lead miner holding a shot-hole boring iron.

(Science Museum / Science and Society Library)